C000100430

OGGY BOYTCHEV escaped from behind the Iron Curtain in 1986. A few months later he joined the BBC in London where he spent the next twenty-five years covering international conflicts. Latterly he became John Simpson's producer, accompanying him on dangerous assignments around the world. His memoir *Simpson & I* chronicles this time. *The Unbeliever* is his first novel. He lives in London.

THE
UNBELIEVER

OGGY BOYTCHEV

QUARTET BOOKS

First published in 2018 by Quartet Books Limited
A member of the Namara Group
27 Goodge Street, London, W1T 2LD

Copyright © Oggy Boytchev 2018

The moral right of the author has been asserted by him in
accordance with the Copyright, Designs and Patents Act, 1988

All rights reserved

No part of this publication may be reproduced, stored in a retrieval system, or
transmitted in any form or by any means, without the prior permission in writing of
the publisher, nor be otherwise circulated in any form of binding or cover other than
that in which it is published and without a similar condition including this condition
being imposed on the subsequent purchaser

A catalogue record for this book is available from the British Library

ISBN 9780704374508

Text design and typesetting by Tetragon, London
Printed and bound in Great Britain by T J International Ltd, Padstow, Cornwall

For my father

Perhaps one did not want to be loved so much as to be understood.

GEORGE ORWELL,
NINETEEN EIGHTY-FOUR

PROLOGUE

'DO YOU PLEAD GUILTY OR NOT GUILTY?'

The stern voice of the chairman of the Supreme Court echoed in the half-empty chamber. It was 26 December 1963. The accused took his time. He looked into the eyes of the presiding judge, then moved his head to meet in turn the eyes of the other five members of the court sitting on either side of the chairman. They avoided his gaze.

The accused was a stout man in his mid-fifties, with short grey hair combed to one side. Dressed in a dark three-piece suit, white shirt and a striped tie, he was flanked by two self-conscious sergeants in the uniform of the People's Militia, the feared police service of the communist regime. His clothes set him apart from the rest of the people in the hall, barely five foot five, but with an intimidatingly elegant demeanour. He had a rough labourer's face, which belied his fierce intelligence.

'Guilty,' he replied in a strong, unwavering voice.

Two heavy television cameras moved quietly on their rails to focus on his face. The regime had allowed the trial to be filmed for a television broadcast on an unspecified day after its close. A few microphones were placed around the room. One, bearing the logo of the national radio, stood in front of the accused to record more clearly his part in the proceedings.

A select group of people were allowed to attend the trial, held in the biggest chamber at the Palais de Justice, the grandest building in Sofia. It was called the Great Ceremonial Hall of the People. Before the presiding judge was able to say anything, the voice of the accused boomed through the loudspeakers again.

'If I have betrayed the Bulgarian people, I deserve the harshest punishment.'

A loud gasp, a cry of anguish from a woman in the audience, was quickly muffled by a handkerchief over her mouth. The television cameras did not move to capture the detail.

'I have been called a traitor, but I have to emphasise that I acted in the interest of the whole of humanity regardless of political ideology,' the man continued, uninterrupted by the judge. 'I am a Marxist. But I did what I did because I believed in the concept of balance in international affairs, the concept that no side should be allowed to think that it has an advantage in the arms race. Otherwise, we are doomed to destroy humankind.'

Uneasy silence descended over the chamber. The word 'concept' was not used in the everyday language of this impoverished Balkan nation. Perhaps not many in the hall, including the judges, had ever used it, but they all understood what it meant.

The presiding judge stood. His face was solemn. His black suit hung uncomfortably, as it would have on most men who had spent their careers in uniform.

'Alexander Ivanov, you have pleaded guilty on charges of treason and espionage in favour of the enemy. In doing so you admit that you have undermined our communist society and you have betrayed not only the Bulgarian people but also the other nations in the brotherhood of socialist countries.' He paused for a second. 'Nonetheless we shall hear the evidence against you in the next few days, as well as any mitigating circumstances that your defence may present. I have to remind you that if this court finds you guilty of the charges as outlined by the prosecution, the sentence that we are mandated to pass in the name of the people is death by firing squad.'

2

There was something sinister and chilling in the way the judge articulated the words 'firing squad'. They were followed by a loud gasp from the same invisible woman in the audience. The sound of shuffling on the audience benches was perhaps a sign of instinctive sympathy for her, but the camera remained focused on the accused. Strict broadcasting guidelines prevented the director from showing what was happening in the audience. The sobbing continued but the distressed woman remained out of shot. Almost as proof that nothing of significance was happening on the visitors' benches, a second camera took a wide-angle shot of the front rows of the hall, giving the impression the room was crowded. A mixture of men in military uniforms and dark suits with stern faces occupied the front three rows. The camera panned slowly from left to right but wouldn't let the viewer see further back.

~

'The hall was almost empty. It wasn't crowded at all.' My companion took her eyes off the screen and adjusted her wide-rimmed spectacles. 'I was sitting just behind the first three official benches. You might've guessed that it was me sobbing.' She spoke with a faint voice that came from the back of her throat.

I looked at her platinum bleached hair, coiffured to a high standard, and wondered whether she had it done this morning before our meeting. She had also applied a faint pink lipstick. A discreet smell of expensive perfume floated gently in the room. She looked like a woman who had never known want in her life. The turbulence of the last sixty years must have miraculously passed her by. Sitting in her comfortable house in the nicest part of town, I didn't think she had ever known hunger or cold even amid the darkest days of the war. The intensity of her face and the alertness of her eyes gave the impression of a woman guarding her secrets jealously. She interrupted the delicate silence: 'How did you get this film?'

'They found it in the Bulgarian National Television archive,' I replied. 'They made a copy for me for a small fee. That's the only footage from the trial they've kept. There may be more in the vaults of the Interior Ministry but I couldn't get access.'

'Why are you interested in my husband's life? He has been airbrushed from history. He has been forgotten and it's probably for the best.'

'As a six-year-old boy, I heard his booming voice from my father's battered old radio,' I said. 'It was a grim winter's morning in a godforsaken provincial town during the January holidays. I was standing in the corner of the only heated room in the house by the old-fashioned wooden radio set, a pre-war German piece of oak-veneered furniture. It shocked me when I heard him plead guilty. My father told me that this man was a hero but in my schoolbooks the heroes never pleaded guilty. They were always right. In my mind, I pictured him as a middle-aged bald man with gold-rimmed spectacles. This was what an international diplomat looked like in my imagination. It's one of those random memories that stick in the mind for the rest of your life.'

'Oh,' she exclaimed and then hesitated. 'I last saw Alexander before he was led away from court after the verdict. He was very calm. We said goodbye. I wasn't allowed to see him again. They didn't give me a body to bury.'

'Did you attend all sessions over the course of the trial?' I asked.

'No, I was there for the public hearings only. The last two sessions were "in camera". The court heard evidence from the foreign minister himself – Alexander's old boss – and other top diplomats, and from members of the Central Committee.' The elderly woman lifted her spectacles above her forehead and looked at the window. The weather promised a beautiful spring day.

4

Her house was situated on the edge of the grandest park in the city, modelled on the great parks of the European capitals. This nation, sitting on the border between East and West, had been desperately trying to assert its European credentials for the last hundred years. The park had been laid out in the early 1880s by Bulgaria's first monarch, Prince Battenberg. The new Bulgaria was carved out of the dying Ottoman Empire in the last quarter of the nineteenth century. It was proud of preserving its identity and ancient roots after five centuries of Ottoman occupation.

Like his new princedom, Alexander of Battenberg straddled the divide between East and West. He was a German prince but also a nephew of the Russian Queen, the tsarina, Maria Alexandrovna. The newly independent Bulgarian state was meant to be an obedient buffer zone between Russia and its arch enemy, the Ottoman Empire. After all, this was why the Russian tsar went to war with the Ottomans in 1877. At the Congress of Berlin the following year the tsar liberator successfully chipped away a small princedom populated by Orthodox Christians, the Bulgars. But no sooner had the fickle Bulgarians gained their independence than they were split down the middle in their allegiances. The nation was divided into Russophiles and Russophobes. This was to remain the curse of Bulgaria, with disastrous consequences in two world wars.

Poor Prince Battenberg couldn't figure out how to sort out this political conundrum and seven years on, despite winning a brilliant military victory against neighbouring Serbia, was forced to abdicate. With uncanny similarity, this would be the fate of every Bulgarian leader in modern history. The nation would adore, ridicule and despise all its leaders in the same ruthless sequence and would never thank them for anything.

When Alexander arrived in Bulgaria to become the country's monarch he was only twenty-two. The young man was full of optimism. After all, this new nation had invited him to become its ruler. A Bulgarian deputation had scoured Europe for suitable candidates and had chosen him. For a while it was a fairy-tale affair. His public appearances drew tears from the eyes of old ladies who admired the beauty of the young prince. He brought refined taste to the formerly provincial city of Sofia.

The fairy-tale prince created a fairy-tale park from scratch and the twenty thousand or so of his subjects living in the new capital were so enchanted by the garden that they called it La Pepiniere, the Nursery. In their eyes, everything French was sophisticated. When the park was later formally named after King Boris III, son of King Ferdinand Saxe-Coburg, the hard-nosed denizens of Sofia, whose romanticism about their new monarchy had evaporated, called it simply the Boris Garden. It became the Freedom Park during my childhood under communism and its name reverted back to the Boris Garden after the fall of the Iron Curtain in 1989.

Unaware of this turbulent history, in which many died in war, uprisings, political murder and repressions, the deciduous oak trees Alexander Battenberg planted here more than 100 years ago were about to unfurl their green leaves yet again and throw their thick shadows over the park.

～

'I'll tell you what I know but I don't have any photographs to show you,' the woman said and leaned back in the soft armchair. 'After Alexander's arrest the secret police took everything connected with him. They didn't leave a single photo. There are hardly any images around to remind people of what he looked like.'

I placed a silver-coloured portable tape recorder on the coffee table in front of her and switched it on.

She looked at it and said, 'That's pretty smart. But I've seen even smaller recording machines. That was a long time ago.' She smiled wryly. 'Where do you want me to begin?'

'Wherever you want,' I said quietly. 'But first, for the record, could you state your name and your relationship to Alexander Ivanov?'

'I am Dora, Alexander's wife...'

She began her story. Every morning over the following few weeks in the spring of 1991 I returned to her house with my tape recorder. Some episodes of her life with Alexander were very vivid in her memory and she kept coming back to them time and time again; others she couldn't remember in detail. Towards the end of the spring I returned to London. Dora died in January the following year. I didn't transcribe the recording for another ten years. My job took me around the world. I found myself in war zones and revolutions with a lot of new exciting stories to tell. But the story of the Cold War spy, Alexander, and his wife, Dora, didn't let go of me.

One day when I was between flights in London, I received a call. A timid male voice asked me if I was still interested in the story of Alexander Ivanov. I jumped up from my seat. The man politely asked me if I would phone him back because he couldn't afford the long-distance call. I didn't catch his name immediately but in a rather formal way he introduced himself as the son of the chief investigator in the case of espionage against Alexander Ivanov. His father had died and left him his secret diaries. As a young ambitious major in the Bulgarian secret service he had made an illegal copy of the interrogation notes in the hope that one day he would write a book about the case. He never did. Two decades after the fall of the Iron Curtain, the son didn't know what to do with his father's diaries. During the Cold War a Western publisher would've paid a fortune for such diaries but now, as the son had discovered, on their own they were worth hardly anything. He had been given my number by a journalist friend of mine in Bulgaria. I accepted his offer to take custody of the diaries.

The diaries contained not only the transcript of the stenographic notes taken during the interrogation but also witty personal observations of the main characters in the affair.

Suddenly, the story came to life. My obsession with Alexander Ivanov's life was finally going to bear some fruit. In my own words, I pieced together Dora's tale and the secret diaries.

I

31 December 1963

'THIS COURT FINDS THE ACCUSED, ALEXANDER IVANOV, BORN in Sofia on 28 March 1907' – the chairman of the Supreme Court was reading from a prepared script – 'guilty of obtaining and collecting state secrets of utmost importance and communicating these secrets wilfully and knowingly to an enemy country: the United States of America. On count One of espionage and treason, according to Article 84, Paragraph 1 of the Penal Code, the court sentences him to death by firing squad. The court also orders the confiscation of all his assets under the same Article.

'On count Two of sabotage and wilfully and knowingly endangering the security of this country, according to Article 77, Paragraph 1 of the Penal Code, the court sentences him to death by firing squad. The court also orders the confiscation of all his assets under the same Article.'

The judge paused. Alexander cocked his head and shot a glance towards the chief prosecutor on the front row to his left. The latter lowered his eyes to avoid his gaze.

The chairman of the Supreme Court continued reading. Over the following few minutes, the judge outlined in greater detail the gravity of Alexander's actions as well as some salacious details about money he had paid to his mistresses in Bulgaria and abroad. The court ordered the bank accounts of his lovers to be frozen and all funds in them confiscated. Finally, the court ordered Alexander to pay the cost of the trial, 387 Lev, which was equivalent to a monthly ministerial salary. Then came the conclusion.

'This verdict is final and cannot be appealed. Alexander Ivanov, you will be taken to Sofia Central Prison where the execution will take place in accordance with the law.'

There was hushed silence in the audience. The chairman nervously collected the pages of his script, while the other members of the panel sat stiffly in their chairs. The two police sergeants stood up and invited Alexander to come with them. He looked helplessly around. The atmosphere in the courtroom was tense. The atmosphere outside even tenser.

For the hard-working citizens of the socialist republic, the world seemed like a more dangerous place. President Kennedy had been assassinated only two months previously. Bulgaria, a little communist country nestled on the outskirts of the Soviet Bloc, bordering two NATO members, Greece and Turkey, was gripped by paranoia, conspiracy and espionage fever. Selective information about the trial of Alexander Ivanov had been released to fan public anger. The American embassy in central Sofia had been attacked by 'angry' crowds carefully manipulated by the regime; windows smashed as the leader of the Young Communist League egged on the crowd from a nearby balcony. The foreign minister, Ivan Bashev, visited the US ambassador and conveyed a personal message advising him to board up the windows and leave the embassy until 'passions subsided'. The ambassador refused. It didn't escape the attention of the Bulgarian authorities that one member of the embassy staff, the second secretary, George Blackwell, had left the country immediately after the announcement of the arrest of Alexander Ivanov.

Alexander Ivanov, a little-known diplomat and a lecturer at the law faculty of Sofia University, had become an overnight media sensation around the world. Most of the Western press was obsessed with the money side of the affair: '$200,000 to a Bulgarian spy to spend on immoral lifestyle', 'The spy who costs America $200,000'. Others proclaimed: 'Full confession of a spy – names and addresses betrayed'. *Pravda* declared succinctly: 'The unmasking of a spy' and 'Setback for American Intelligence'.

During his spectacular demise, Alexander Ivanov had been stripped of all his official positions. He was no longer an employee of the Foreign Ministry. He had been removed from the staff of the law faculty where he was an assistant professor. But he still held the post of chairman of the International Institute of Space Law, otherwise known as the International Space Federation. This was a job dear to his heart. It reflected his abilities and ambitions, and his standing in the world. It was not in the gift of the communist authorities to remove him from this position.

2

3 September 1963

Metropol Hotel, Moscow

ALEXANDER IVANOV CALLED ROOM SERVICE. HE WAS VERY particular about the sandwiches. 'Salad Olivier with ham, not chicken,' he said in a stern voice. 'And tea with honey, not sugar, and a few slices of lemon.' He was pleased that his immaculate Russian, although spoken with a slight foreign accent, commanded respect from the staff at the hotel. After asserting his authority, he would normally have a friendly word or two with the female voice on the other end of the line. A useful chat-up line would be something about traditional Russian cuisine. But now he didn't have time for that routine.

He was in Moscow for the latest session of the International Space Federation. His Soviet hosts had been so obliging when he'd requested his favourite, the Metropol. Most pleasing. It was not just that the hotel was a five-minute walk to the Bolshoi Theatre and the Kremlin; in his mind the building represented everything he liked in life – authority, opulence, decadence. He loved the wide marble staircase and the grand rooms, but above all came the facade, a fine example of Art Nouveau architecture. On the gable above the main entrance glittered a magnificent mosaic panel. One had to step back from the road to see it in all its glory. There was a bench on the opposite side of Teatralniy Proyezd, on the corner with Theatre Square, from where he could study every detail whenever he had the time.

The creator of the mosaic called it the *Princess of the Dream*, an alluring subject that was not lost on Alexander's imagination. It tells the eternal story of unrequited love – the unattainable princess appears to the dying knight in his last moments. She floats over him depicted in the cold blue colour of a corpse. The artist, Mikhail Vrubel, one of the most controversial pre-revolutionary Russian painters, was both admired and reviled for the 'wild ugliness' of his works. The demonic passion of the *Princess of the Dream* stirred Alexander's soul every time he looked at it. But there was no time now. He was expecting a visitor. His chest heaved with anticipation.

Olga was a young physicist he had met at last year's session of the Federation. He had spotted her fresh face a few times in the audience. She met his eyes on a couple of occasions but it wasn't until the last cocktail party at the end of the conference that he spoke to her. It was a hot summer's evening on the Black Sea coast, at a resort outside the Bulgarian city of Varna. Delegates milled around on the veranda of the hotel overlooking the sea. Olga wore a black dress, revealing the alabaster skin on her shoulders. Dizzy with success – he had just been elected as chairman of the Federation – and emboldened by a few glasses of Bulgarian sparkling wine, he braved the age gap and spoke to her. She was standing alone, propped against the balustrade, and looked like she was ready to leave the party at any moment. Expertly, he posed a question: what had impressed her most at the conference? She looked him in the eye without a trace of fear. He knew the answer.

She spoke about how enthralled she was by his speech on the principles of Roman law. He had taken his expertise and applied it to the uncharted territory of space exploration. He was working with Soviet and American lawyers, and the goal was an international treaty for the peaceful exploration of outer space. They sat on the concrete steps and she listened.

It was the Romans who first developed the idea of *ius cogens*, or the peremptory norm, from which no exemptions were allowed. Over the last hundred years it had grown into the fundamental principle of international law. The principle overrode even national sovereignty, he said. Individual states would not be allowed to do whatever they want in space. The cosmos would be a place for mutual cooperation and peaceful coexistence. The treaty, he smiled, would be ready to be signed by the Soviet Union and the United States in the next two to three years, and then all countries in the world would join.

He talked and Olga listened. Alexander liked that.

Later, in his hotel room, they didn't talk about Roman law. While he was undressing her, he asked about the place she grew up and her family. She said that she didn't know her father. He had been a young officer in the Red Army, stationed in her mother's village in eastern Russia just before the war. Like many others, Olga was a Russian war baby. But she was bright. She did well at school. She was good at maths and physics and look where she was now.

Alexander was experienced enough to know that anybody sent to represent the Soviet state abroad must be reporting to the KGB. But he didn't care about such trivial detail. Fate had offered him a chance to have an affair with a good-looking young woman. It would be stupid not to take it. She was an intelligent, highly educated physicist and that was a bonus. He liked intelligent women. There was nothing of importance that she could tell the KGB about him.

Olga had a curvy figure and was a passionate lover. She wasn't a stunning beauty, not the type to make heads turn when she walked past in the street. But she had deep blue eyes, blonde hair and very firm breasts. Alexander was under no illusion that she slept with him for his looks. That's why he was very generous to her. He had always been generous to his lovers. This would be his third meeting with Olga and he was looking forward to it.

There was a knock on the door. Alexander didn't want to be seen to be answering it too quickly, so he tried to find something to do. He took off his jacket and threw it on the sofa. He would look more casual and masculine in a white shirt. Then, when he finally opened the door, his world collapsed.

Three men in long trench coats stood before him. He knew exactly what was happening. In a way, he had been expecting it for some time. But why now? And where was Olga? Could she be part of it?

A youthful man, hatless and with a mass of brown hair, appeared from behind the three KGB agents: he wore a Bulgarian State Security uniform and said, 'Alexander Ivanov, we have a warrant for your arrest.'

Before he finished Alexander moved backwards to allow the four men to enter the room. One of the agents took position in front of the closed door.

'I am Major Ivan Ohridski, Bulgarian State Security,' the young man said. 'We also have a warrant to search this room.'

Alexander didn't utter a word, he just shrugged his shoulders contemptuously. By the time the KGB agents had finished their job, Alexander was already waiting by the window fully dressed in a thick dark coat. He was holding his black felt hat in his hand. He threw one last glance through the window as if to say goodbye to the city he was so fond of.

Major Ohridski was unnerved by Alexander's disdain. In his previous experience, people were reduced to gibbering wrecks when the KGB descended on them.

The elderly watchwoman at the end of the corridor whose job was to keep an eye on who came in and out of the rooms looked down as Alexander passed in front of her little desk. Those elevated desks were found on every floor in every international hotel in the Soviet Union. The case of a high-flying apparatchik's fall from grace was all too familiar to her. Recently she'd heard rumours that Suslov and Brezhnev were plotting against Khrushchev. Mikoyan was in with the plotters, too. She, like many other Russians, had learned to read between the lines of what the party newspaper, *Pravda*, had been saying. There was talk of collective leadership, scientific planning, failure in agriculture and need for economic reform. These were new matters, and they foreshadowed change. She craved stability. In a matter of months the plotters would succeed, and by this time next year Khrushchev would be gone.

Downstairs, Alexander looked at the portrait of Khrushchev above the solid oak reception desk and shook his head. The jolly peasant smile, the glistening bald head and the four shiny gold stars on his chest made him cringe. He had always disliked the man. He found him uncouth and dangerous.

What happened next took Major Ohridski by surprise. It happened so quickly that he had no time to react. He was not sure what was expected of him. A black Volga pulled up in front of the hotel entrance. Alexander Ivanov was swiftly bundled into the back seat by two of the KGB officers and it drove away at speed towards the Lubyanka. The third operative remained with Major Ohridski. A few seconds later another vehicle pulled up slowly and the agent said politely that he was going to accompany the major to Sheremetyevo airport, where he was to wait for the arrested man. There was an Ilyushin Il-14 on standby to take them back to Bulgaria. Major Ohridski was puzzled but knew better than to ask any questions. His Soviet comrades must know what they were doing. This case was going to be very tricky. Very tricky indeed.

3

FORTY-EIGHT HOURS LATER

ALEXANDER IVANOV ARRIVED AT SHEREMETYEVO IN A DIFferent KGB vehicle, this time a small green military GAZ. He was accompanied by two uniformed men. Although he was accused of the gravest crime of espionage, which carried an automatic death sentence, it struck Major Ohridski that Alexander was never handcuffed.

The major himself had spent the last two days and nights at the KGB hotel within the secure perimeter of the airport. The room was very comfortable and the airport canteen served excellent food. He had received one phone call from Bulgaria. The chief prosecutor was inquiring on behalf of the Leader about the delay. But when he heard that the KGB had taken Alexander Ivanov to the Lubyanka and the Bulgarian major had been ordered to wait at the airport, there were no further questions. He had to wait.

The ambitious young major spent most of his time in his room studying the file, which his colleagues at State Security in Sofia had compiled for him. The case was far from clear. Alexander Ivanov was accused of being an American spy. But what was the evidence? A professional Hammarlund radio set was found in his apartment in Sofia. A code card on the shelf above the radio suggested that he had been sending coded transmissions to the Americans. It was believed that a NATO listening station in northern Greece, close to the Bulgarian border, was the target of Alexander's messages. Agents who had tailed him had reported that he had met the second secretary of the American embassy, George Blackwell, several times inside the Russian bookshop opposite the Army Club in Sofia. But that was not going to be enough. There was going to be an open trial, he was told. Foreign journalists would be invited. The major's task was to prepare the ground for a full public confession. The propaganda machine would do the rest. Alexander's character would be besmirched. He would be portrayed as a rapacious and immoral capitalist stooge. Alexander's lover in Sofia, Tonka Karabasheva, a famous scientist in the field of tuberculosis, had already admitted receiving large sums of money from him. Another of his lovers, Rosa Aronova, had emigrated to Israel but it was hard to verify allegations that he was paying the mortgage on her apartment in Tel Aviv. The assumption was that the money came from the Americans. But something was bothering the major. After all, Alexander was a well-paid diplomat. He had been earning hard currency in the last seven years and had been living off expenses. He didn't have any children. His wife was a well-known doctor, frequently travelling to medical symposia in the West. It was a requirement of Alexander's job that he met foreign diplomats.

The major thought that there was something else missing. Why was Alexander put under surveillance last year? Initial suspicions must have come from the Soviet side, but there was no record of this in the file. And now this bizarre behaviour by the KGB, and all without a word of explanation for him. The unexpected delay was causing anxiety among the top brass in Bulgaria. When he was given the job, Major Ohridski was told that he must extract a confession. So that was the plan.

The Ilyushin Il-14 was waiting on the tarmac, propellers idle.

'What a beauty!' Alexander exclaimed, looking up at the shiny aluminium body of the aircraft lit up by the floodlights of the airport building. He was going to travel in style yet again. A night flight to Sofia in a swish thirty-two-seater furnished for Soviet VIPs was something he would enjoy with gusto, even if it was going to be the last journey of his life.

When they settled in the cabin, Major Ohridski said: 'You probably don't remember me, but I attended your lectures at the law faculty in '55.'

Alexander turned his head and looked at the major's face, studying it with curiosity. 'You must have been a mature student. How old are you?'

'I'm thirty-eight but I was thirty when I studied for a law degree at Sofia University. Before that I did a two-year course at the State Security Academy. I joined the Interior Ministry troops, the People's Militia, at the age of eighteen, back in 1944 when the fascist regime was overthrown. I knew your name when I worked at the Militia, although we never met. You were the chief secretary to the Interior Ministry.'

Alexander didn't reply. Of course, he didn't remember the major. He never remembered any of his male students. The girls, though, oh the girls he remembered very well, not least because there were so few of them. For five years he was banished into academia after a fallout with the regime. It was the time of witch-hunts against the 'enemy within the party' and he was lucky that the only thing that happened to him was losing his job in the diplomatic service. Others had not been so fortunate.

'I would like to ask you a few questions,' Major Ohridski said, and placed the cardboard file on the pull-out table in front of him. Alexander, sitting opposite, closed his eyes. He wasn't feeling well. Events over the last forty-eight hours had set off his stomach ulcer. He hadn't changed his shirt for three days. There was a slight whiff of alcohol about him. It was obvious to the major that the interrogation at the Lubyanka had been an uncharacteristically friendly one, helped along with a few shots of vodka. What was it his KGB colleagues were keeping from him?

'I'm tired. I haven't taken my blood pressure medication for a few days. I need it, I might have a stroke otherwise.'

'OK, you can have some rest. The flight will take ten hours. We'll be stopping in Kiev, Odessa and Bucharest before arriving in Sofia. There will be plenty of time to talk.'

Alexander leaned back in his seat and closed his eyes. There was something worrying about this circuitous route. He had done the Moscow to Sofia flight in an Il-14 without any stoppages for refuelling. The major must have been instructed to tire him out and extract an easy confession before arrival in Sofia. Would they let him sleep?

He listened to the hum of the engines and an overwhelming calm settled on him. His body felt weightless. The stewardess looked lovely in her blue uniform. If it hadn't been for the two uniformed KGB operatives behind him and that pushy major, this could have been a very pleasant journey. He liked to travel. He had been on the move all his life. But now he was tired. He wanted to put an end to all this. He wanted to sleep.

When he woke a short time later, Major Ohridski adopted a more aggressive attitude.

'When did you become a spy for the CIA and what are the names of your contacts at the agency?'

'Can I have some water? I'm very thirsty,' Alexander said.

'You can have water and food after you answer my questions.'

'These are nonsensical questions. I have never been a spy for anybody. I have no contacts with the CIA.'

'This is not true,' Major Ohridski said, raising his voice. 'We have hard evidence of your espionage activities.'

'If you have such evidence, why are you asking me these questions? I have nothing to add to what I just said. Now, can I have some water?'

'We shall present you with the evidence on our arrival in Sofia. It shows that you have passed valuable information to the enemy.

According to our constitution, this is treason and is punishable by death.'

Alexander shook his head. 'What do you want from me? I am tired, I am thirsty, and I need my medication.' The loud noise of the aircraft engine hitting turbulence drowned out his last words.

There was a pause. The two KGB officers at the back stirred.

'We can finish everything here and now,' the major pressed again. 'Confess your crimes and you can have water, food and medication. You can do that at a stroke. One, two, three, done!'

'You're talking nonsense,' Alexander said contemptuously.

'Do you know what?' the major changed tack. 'The leaders of our country think very highly of you. They respect you. You are very well connected. But don't think that anybody will shed any tears for you. No one will help you. I am the only one who can assist you right now. A voluntary confession and cooperation with us will go a long way towards convincing the court of mitigating circumstances.'

'Has my wife been told about my arrest?' Alexander took the major by surprise. 'Has she been told about the accusations?'

Major Ohridski realised that Alexander was a true professional. He was able to run rings around him even in his current state. What about when he was rested and had time to think?

'Why are you worried about your wife now? You should've worried about her when you started your vile activities…'

'I would like to know what her condition is at the moment. Did she faint when you told her about my arrest? Is she in hospital? I am worried about her health.'

'I don't have to answer your questions. You are under arrest, not me. But if you confess, all this will change. You will see your wife, you'll get your medication, and the stewardess will bring you some water.'

'Confess what?' Alexander asked.

'Well, let's start with something like: who were you in regular contact with when you worked at the United Nations? Was there anybody else from our mission in New York who was also a spy?'

'Well, let me think,' Alexander said with a serious look on his face. 'I was in regular contact with the Secretary-General of the UN, U Thant, with the head of the economic commission, with the American representative at the Nuclear Energy Committee in Geneva...'

'This is not going to work,' Major Ohridski interrupted him. He called on the stewardess to bring some water and food. Alexander ate without appetite.

An hour later the aircraft reached the stop-off point in Kiev. The major offered to let Alexander stretch his legs on the tarmac during refuelling but Alexander, pale and dishevelled, felt too tired to make it out of the plane. During the second leg of the journey from Kiev to Odessa, Alexander was spared the questioning. He tried to get to sleep but couldn't. At Odessa, the plane was held up: no one could explain the reason for the delay, and for the first time Alexander betrayed his anxiety. The major again invited him to take a stroll, and again Alexander refused.

'You realise that there'll be another stop in Bucharest, before we make it to Sofia?'

The major's high-pitched voice and provincial accent were wearing Alexander down. He changed his mind and left the plane to have a short walk on the tarmac, accompanied by the two sullen KGB officers.

Once airborne en route to Bucharest, the major resumed the interrogation.

'Would you tell me who gave you the code for the radio communications with the CIA?'

'I don't know what you are talking about,' Alexander replied calmly.

'Well, you see, you have a problem here. A code card was found during the forensic search of your apartment in Sofia. Our experts can prove that you have used this code. Specialist radio equipment was found in your apartment. Again, our experts will prove that this equipment was used to receive and transmit coded messages.'

'This is nonsense. If you are talking about my Hammarlund radio, I bought it in New York because I like to listen to opera in superior sound quality. I have an import licence for it, as well as for the two large speakers, which no doubt you will have noticed in my flat.'

The major made two further attempts to extract a confession from Alexander Ivanov during the long flight from Moscow to Sofia, both expertly rebuffed by the accused. Around midday on Friday 6 September 1963 the special Ilyushin Il-14 aircraft operated by the Soviet KGB landed at Sofia airport.

The weather was pleasantly warm and the sky looked as if it were made of light blue silk. The airport was decked out with flags and huge posters of the country's communist leaders: a national holiday was fast approaching. 9 September was the anniversary of the pro-Soviet *coup d'état* of 1944, when the communist takeover of the country began. The three biggest canvas posters which greeted the arrivals at the airport were portraits of Marx, Engels and Lenin, followed by smaller pictures of the members of the Bulgarian politburo. They were arranged in alphabetical order.

That's what they mean by collective leadership, Alexander thought. His eyes moved towards the end of the row and rested on the face of Todor Zhivkov, a youngish, nondescript clean-shaven face he had known for a long time. Alexander's friends called him the Fox. This wily man had already assumed the two most powerful positions in the land – first secretary of the Communist Party and prime minister. The portrait of Alexander's old boss at the Interior Ministry back in 1944, Anton Yugov, was noticeable by its absence. He had been removed the previous year and for the following thirty years he would live out a comfortable retirement in total obscurity. Zhivkov never killed his opponents. He stuffed their mouths with gold.

Back in those fateful days of September 1944, Yugov had taken control of the notorious Interior Ministry. Alexander arrived at the door of the ministry two days after the old government had fallen. In the two years following the coup Alexander served under Yugov, that simple and uneducated man who showed insatiable cruelty exterminating the enemies of the Communist Party. He didn't hesitate to kill or imprison even some of those military officers who had helped the communists in the anti-fascist coup. Although Alexander believed in the abstract idea of communism, he shuddered at the memory of those cruel years. He felt a sharp pain in his left knee. Arthritis, his doctor had told him.

Although he and his wife had recently separated, his many infidelities finally tipping the balance, the only person he wanted to see now was her. Dora was his soulmate, his teenage sweetheart. Would they allow a visit?

Still standing on the tarmac, Alexander turned his head south towards Vitosha Mountain, which loomed large over the airport, almost out of proportion, more like a stage prop made of polystyrene than a real thing. For the first time since his arrest he lost concentration. Anxiety crept up inside his chest. He had a premonition that this would be the last time he would gaze on his beloved mountain, under whose shadow he had grown up.

4

Dora Ivanov

WHEN ALEXANDER CAME TO OUR PROVINCIAL TOWN IN MAY
1925 he was something of a novelty. Eighteen years old and from
the capital, Sofia, he talked confidently about art, politics and
literature. He brought with him avant-garde poetry magazines.
He wore different clothes.

His father, a prominent liberal lawyer, had decided to get out of
Sofia along with his family. Terrible things were happening there.

On 16 April 1925, a group of communists had blown up the
church of Sveta Nedelya in an attempt to kill King Boris III. In
fact, the whole scheme was more elaborate. Two days earlier the
plotters had assassinated a prominent general. They knew that
the funeral would take place at Sveta Nedelya and the King was
bound to attend. As it happened, the King was out of town on
the day of the funeral. When the plotters detonated the smuggled
explosives packed into the bell tower, the dome collapsed on the
congregation. The church was packed. Poison gas had been mixed
with the explosives, and more than 200 people died in this single
act of violence – the biggest terrorist attack the world had seen
to date. The top brass of the Bulgarian military was eliminated
at a stroke. Three people were promptly arrested and hanged,
including the sexton of the church, who was a communist sym-
pathiser. He confessed that he had allowed the plotters to hide
the explosives in the bell tower and had given them the timetable
of the service.

There followed a wave of extrajudicial killings and disappearances. Murderous gangs roamed the capital, killing and torturing anybody accused of leftist political views. A few days after the bombing, Alexander's family boarded the train to Stara Zagora; to avoid suspicion they took no luggage. They were coming to stay with Alexander's grandparents, who had a big and comfortable house, one of the nicest in town.

'Stalin didn't approve of the bombing,' Alexander argued with a group of students at the high school, where he was immediately admitted to finish the year. 'In fact, I know that he ordered the Bulgarian Communist Party not to do it. But they ignored his orders.'

'How do you know that?' I asked.

This was the first time I spoke to him. He looked at me and the fire in his eyes died down. He smiled. 'In fact, I don't know that. I only heard it from a friend of my father's. Well, I shouldn't be telling you that. They'll set the Macedonian dogs on me.'

No one laughed. The students knew what he meant. A group of anti-communist nationalists calling itself the Internal Macedonian Revolutionary Organisation was doing the dirty work for the right-wing government. Their favourite methods were beheadings or breaking the victim's skull with a wooden club. Shooting somebody in the head was only reserved for situations when the execution had to be done in a hurry.

Alexander wasn't a good-looking boy. He was short, but had big hands and a square jaw. His mousy hair was always in a mess. But he knew how to charm the girls with serious talk. In the summer of 1925, he talked about the proletarian revolution, the abolition of the class system and the dialectics of Hegel. I would learn later – much later – that over that summer the innocent-faced eighteen-year-old Alexander had made his grandfather's maid pregnant. I never found out what happened with the baby.

I couldn't give him any children after we got married, so I didn't want to know. His father might've paid for an abortion. But I knew that Alexander kept sending small amounts of money to that woman until his last days. This was the kind of person he was.

Oblivious to all that, I thought he had chosen me. We went to the cinema. We ate ice cream in the municipal garden in the evenings. And we talked. He would walk me to the front gate at night and we would stand there in the balmy summer evenings and talk. I have to admit that these were the best days of my life.

In the autumn, Alexander's father sent him back to Sofia to study law at the university but the rest of the family remained in Stara Zagora. In fact, his father never wanted to move back to the capital. The law firm he had established in Zagora was very successful. They had a large, comfortable house of their own, and the family enjoyed a quiet life.

During the first year at the university Alexander wrote occasional letters, but we never met up. By the end of 1926, the persecution of suspected communist sympathisers abated. Families affected by the violent backlash became resigned to the idea that they would never find out what had happened to the disappeared. Occasional high-profile cases were taken up in the left-wing press, but people were glad that there were no more death squads roaming the streets. I was looking forward to starting my medical studies in Sofia, hoping that I'd get closer to Alexander again.

Even at that tender age when I was confused between love and lust, I knew that I wanted to marry him. I never felt bored in his company; I wanted to listen to his voice, I wanted his big hands to hold me. No one else had looked at me with such desire as he did during that summer. It is such a good fortune to be wanted.

I couldn't wait to go to Sofia for my studies because I simply had to see him again.

Then I received the devastating news that Alexander was going to Paris to continue his law degree at the Sorbonne. I thought that I would never see him again.

5

9 September 1963

Major Ohridski began the first session of the inter-rogation: 'Alexander Ivanov, I would like to start by asking you a simple question. You can answer with yes or no. Do you know the name George Duvall?'

Alexander shrugged his shoulders.

'Is that a yes or a no?'

'What date is it today?' Alexander asked.

'9 September,' answered the major mechanically.

'So, it is Revolution Day. Nineteen years since we took power in this country. And you are not at the parade?' Alexander said ironically.

The major ignored this. But his face froze. After a few seconds his intense expression relaxed and he took a deep breath.

'Well, we know that George Duvall is you,' he said trium-phantly. 'This is the code name the CIA gave you.' He didn't give Alexander any time to respond and continued: 'Do the names Anderson and Bonar mean anything to you? George Blackwell? Perhaps you could start by telling us about what exactly your work for the CIA involved.'

There was a pause. The major knew that he had scored a point. All the training he had received from the Soviet comrades was going to pay off. He needed to find a chink in the armour of this experienced diplomat and then prize him open like a tin of sardines. They sat in silence. The tape recorder on the table was running but the major knew that outside, in an adjacent room, a stenographer was recording the conversation on paper too.

The major pretended to look for something in the folder in front of him. He took out a single sheet of paper, yellow with age, and held it in front of his eyes as if studying the tightly typed text. At the top there were various official stamps and handwritten initials. It looked like this letter had stopped at many desks and passed through many hands. Alexander recognised it as the diplomatic paper used during the time of his work at the Bulgarian embassy in Paris.

'OK then,' the major finally said. 'Can we start with Madame Lucienne Bovren? How long have you known her?'

Alexander knew very well who Madame Bovren was. Their acquaintance, no, no, their friendship, went further back than the years he spent at the embassy in Paris. It went right back to his student days at the Sorbonne in 1927. Lucienne was almost twenty years older than him but he didn't mind. She helped him discover Paris in the late 1920s and he discovered life.

Paris then seemed like the centre of the universe. It was the city of avant-garde culture, attracting the most talented and the most controversial artists, writers and musicians in the world. The young student from Sofia took his modest lodgings in the vicinity of Place de la Contrescarpe in the Latin Quarter. It was a run-down working-class area but it was close to the law department at the Sorbonne. His father's allowance, which he received from the bank every month, didn't stretch very far.

74 rue de Cardinal Lemoine was a dilapidated house but it was at the heart of bohemian Paris. The culture of the Left Bank was in the very air. You could smell it, you could breathe it. In those days Ernest Hemingway, James Joyce, Salvador Dalí, Man Ray, René Magritte, Luis Buñuel and even George Orwell found their homes on the Left Bank.

But Alexander was removed from this international crowd. Initially, he lived in a Bulgarian bubble of mainly left-wing expats. In that little group, he met the incredibly talented composer Lyubomir Pipkov, who studied music with Nadia Boulanger at Ecole Normale de Musique de Paris, and the political émigré Milko Tarabanov, who had escaped from internment in Bulgaria. Pipkov came from an eminent musical family, and despite his young age he had already composed several piano concerti and was destined for fame and fortune. He was obsessed with Bulgarian folk music and unashamedly borrowed themes and scores in order to create music for the masses. He was never short of money and was very generous to his friends.

Tarabanov, on the other hand, was a professional revolutionary. He had joined the youth wing of the Bulgarian Communist Party at the tender age of fifteen and had been in police custody many times. He had made his way to France when he was just twenty-two. When Alexander met him, he was already a member of the French Communist Party.

During the first year in Paris, Alexander spent most of his time at the Sorbonne. He worked incredibly hard to justify his father's considerable expense in sending him to France. Occasionally, he went to meetings of French communists and walked the streets of Paris, absorbing every detail of the city. To a young man like him looking for love, Paris had a lot more to offer than Sofia. He had hoped to see the Russian prima ballerina, Anna Pavlova, in a production by the Ballets Russes and was saddened to learn from the newspapers that she had fallen ill in The Hague. He stared longingly at posters of the half-naked jazz singer and dancer Josephine Baker in her trademark banana costume. He saved enough money to buy a ticket to see her at the Folies Bergère. Baker had arrived from St. Louis two years before, in 1925, for the Exposition des Arts Decoratifs, and had taken Paris by storm. That exhibition, along the esplanade of Les Invalides, had drawn a crowd of sixteen million people, and the term Art Deco was born. Ever since, Paris had been plastered with posters of the enticing Josephine, the Creole Goddess. Alexander loved the show.

One day Tarabanov took him to a meeting where the French Communist Party secretary, Maurice Thorez, gave a speech denouncing Leon Trotsky. The meeting was held in a cinema in the working-class stronghold of Belleville. Alexander liked the passion with which Thorez defended Stalin and issued his plea for all workers of the world to unite under Stalin's leadership. But, after the meeting, something more momentous happened.

As they spilled out of the cinema, a group of well-dressed people from the meeting were in the midst of an animated debate in the street. As they passed by, a young man turned to them and said: 'What country do you come from, comrades?' After a short exchange, the two Bulgarians were invited to join the group in a cafe in the main street, rue de Belleville. Here Alexander was introduced to Lucienne Bovren.

Lucienne said that she was an arts teacher. While the others were wrapped up in a political discussion, Alexander summoned all his courage and launched into a monologue, quoting randomly from the poetry magazines he used to read in Sofia. Lucienne listened. Her big brown eyes focussed on his. He didn't look away. His speech quickened and his face flushed. Finally, he reached his favourite topic – sexual desire in symbolist aesthetics. How many times had Lucienne seen the arrogance of youth before? Alexander had forgotten that she was an arts teacher and spoke as if he were the greatest expert on symbolism. 'The fruit of death upon the tree of life,' he proclaimed, 'was used to denounce the malign power of sexual desire in art.' They both smiled when he announced triumphantly that he couldn't disagree more with such a philosophical postulate. In the following two years, until

Alexander's departure from Paris, their relationship flourished. Lucienne was no beauty, but for Alexander she exuded femininity. She was everything he wanted in a woman. She was intelligent, kind, accommodating, gentle, and she loved having sex with him. She told him that she was once married but the marriage didn't work out. For her, marriage was another form of class oppression.

Lucienne lived in Montmartre. She earned enough money as a teacher to rent a small apartment not far from Sacre Coeur. Alexander envied her lifestyle. She was free to do anything she wanted. They met only two or three times a month but that was enough for him. He never suspected that she was an agent for Deuxième Bureau (French Intelligence). But as he would later learn upon his return to Bulgaria, most communist movements, including the one in Bulgaria, had been infiltrated by the police. Much, much later, after the war had ended, they met again. She sought him out during his first official assignment in Paris on behalf of the new communist government of Bulgaria. She had aged but he still found her attractive.

'Do you know what this is?' Major Ohridski interrupted the silence and waved the document in front of him. 'This is a report from a member of staff at the Bulgarian embassy in Paris. It says that in 1947 you were spotted on a bridge in Paris in the company of a well-dressed older woman. You were followed to her apartment. The embassy official found out the name of that woman. Madame Lucienne Bovren, an agent of the French secret service.'

'Of course, I know Lucienne Bovren. She was a member of the French Communist Party. I first met her when I was a student in Paris. Pipkov and Tarabanov know her, too. They can tell you how all three of us met her after a gathering of the French Communist Party at which Maurice Thorez gave a speech.'

'Name dropping will not help you. Pipkov and Tarabanov will not be called as witnesses. The best thing to do is to admit that you have been a foreign spy.'

'Nonsense,' Alexander retorted. 'Why wasn't I punished after some half-wit busybody at our embassy sent such vulgar smears against me? Ah, I know. This is because our government knew that Madame Bovren had helped me establish direct contact with the prime minister of France, Leon Blum, in 1947. Do you know what that means in diplomatic terms? It's a diplomatic coup. They should've given me a medal for that, not denounced me.'

The major put the paper down and looked Alexander in the eye.

'Enough for today. I've promised to take my son to the fireworks tonight.'

6

DORA IVANOV

THE COUNTRY WOKE UP ON THE MORNING OF 19 MAY 1934 to the news that there had been a *coup d'état*. The phone lines were dead and the electricity cut off. We heard the rumbling of tank engines and the metallic rattle of tank tracks hitting the cobblestone streets in the distance. It sounded like the centre of the city had been occupied by armoured regiments. The radio played patriotic military marches, interrupted from time to time by an announcement on behalf of the army. They told us to keep calm and stay at home. The constitution had been suspended and parliament dissolved. All public gatherings were banned.

Rumours reached us of a disturbance around the royal palace. We didn't know what to make of it. Alexander thought it was a fascist military coup intended to bring Bulgaria closer in alignment to Hitler. But by 9 a.m. there was a surprise. The radio announced that the King had signed a decree appointing Kimon Georgiev, a well-known anti-monarchist, as prime minister. Georgiev was a decorated veteran from World War I, in which he had lost an eye. He had links with the Communist Party and we knew that he favoured establishing diplomatic relations with the Soviet Union. By lunchtime, it became clear that a shadowy group of republican military officers calling themselves 'Zveno' ('the Unit'), had seized power. They declared that they controlled the entire country and were going to rule by decree.

Alexander and I were newlyweds. We were both twenty-seven. Our wedding was a low-key affair. Alexander didn't want a church service but his parents insisted. As a dutiful son, he didn't like to displease his father so he agreed. Only the closest family on both sides had gathered at the Church of St Sofia, an ancient red-brick basilica in the centre of the city. Alexander's family had chosen the most prestigious venue. My heart fluttered when I walked down the aisle. I was marrying the man whose presence always made me happy. He didn't have to tell me that he loved me. I felt it every time he looked at me, then and later, even to his last days.

He was now a trainee solicitor in the firm of a left-wing lawyer, Nissim Mevorah, one of the very few legal practices that offered to defend people indicted under the notorious State Security Act. These were mainly communists and anarchists charged with sedition.

Upon his return from Paris in 1929, Alexander seemed like a different person: grown up, mature, calmer. His father had seen his fortune disappear in the stock market crash that sparked the Great Depression, and the allowance he used to send him to Paris had dried up. Alexander was angry. His father's bankruptcy had a profound effect on him. He kept saying that when the communist revolution succeeded productivity would be so high that people would be able to enjoy the fruits of their labour without having to resort to banks and the stock market.

But I felt that something else had happened during those two years in Paris. Emotionally, he became less excitable, more intro-vert, almost secretive. He reluctantly went back to the law faculty of Sofia University to finish his degree. Gone were the days when he would engage in a random political argument with people he hardly knew. He kept his politics to himself. That didn't mean that he had given up the struggle. On the contrary, he was elected as the first chairman of the People's Student Union, an organisation inspired by the banned Communist Party. He was more pragmatic, more professional in his revolutionary work. He was regularly in touch with party workers who had channels to the Soviet Union, who conveyed direct messages from Stalin. Although the Student Union had renounced violence in order to gain official registration and be allowed to operate openly, it had one aim – to recruit students for the worldwide communist struggle under the leadership of Joseph Stalin. Both of us were founding members. Most of our meetings took place in the open air – out in the countryside or in the mountains. We disguised them as picnics. Girls and boys together, free love, you know.

We had dated for a few years. There was one thing about Alexander that marked him out from the other boys. When I was with him I felt that I was the only girl in the world. He gave me his undivided attention. But it wasn't just the physical attraction. We were both enthralled by the idea of communism. We wanted to change the world. We believed the revolution would bring about happiness to everyone. With hindsight, it's easy to dismiss our idealism but back then it was real. We both felt it in our bones. We loved each other and it seemed that we were destined to be together. I was a student at the medical faculty. He was going to be a lawyer, defending people from injustice. I was going to be a doctor helping the poor and the infirm. We were the perfect couple. And by the beginning of 1934 we were already married.

As I said, we believed the worldwide revolution was near. The dark clouds gathering over Europe were just the harbinger of revolution. Hitler was elected Chancellor in Germany. Alexander and I thought that only communism and Stalin's Russia could save us from the fascists. And we were very proud when Stalin appointed a Bulgarian communist, Georgi Dimitrov, as head of the Communist International, the Comintern.

Dimitrov was probably the most famous communist in the world at the time – after Stalin, of course. At the beginning of 1933 he found himself accused, together with two other Bulgarians and a Dutchman, of setting fire to the Reichstag in Berlin in order to start a communist revolution. Following the fire a state of emergency was declared across Germany, which gave Hitler a free hand to destroy the German Communist Party. Dimitrov became a cause célèbre when he refused to accept an appointed barrister and defended himself during the so-called Reichstag Fire Trial held in Leipzig. Famously, he cross-examined Hermann Göring, who, as president of the Reichstag, took the stand to accuse the Comintern of deliberately starting the fire. Dimitrov stood up to him and in perfect German not only demolished his legal arguments but defended communism as 'the most progressive ideology' in the world. The anti-fascist press around the globe reprinted a famous headline: 'There is only one brave man in Germany and he is Bulgarian'. It wasn't clear who first came up with it. Despite being known to the German police as senior members of the Comintern, Dimitrov and his two Bulgarian friends were acquitted. This was the last trial heard by independent judges from the old Imperial High Court in Germany. The Dutchman, Marinus van der Lubbe, caught in the act of setting fire to the building, was sentenced to death. Within days, he was beheaded by guillotine, the customary method of execution in the state of Saxony at the time.

Dimitrov and his two Bulgarian companions were sentenced to nine months in prison for residing in Germany illegally under false identities. All three went back to Moscow after serving their sentences. Dimitrov was rewarded with the top job at the Comintern. The other two were caught up in Stalin's purges. One of them, Tanev, died in a labour camp. The other, Popov, survived seventeen years in the Gulag. Crippled with illness, he returned to

Bulgaria where he died in obscurity. His memoirs were smuggled out of the country in 1984 and published in Paris.

~

'Do you know what Nissim has just told me?' Alexander whispered. It was the night after the 1934 coup. Despite the newly imposed curfew, he had sneaked out through the back garden after dark and gone to Mevorah's house to talk about the putsch. Anybody caught in the streets after sunset without a pass would be arrested. But we were desperately trying to figure out what was happening and what direction the new rulers would take. On that spring night our foreboding was that the country would be pushed closer and closer in alliance with Hitler. 'The plotters had planned to execute the royal family and proclaim a republic,' he said. 'A tank regiment loyal to the plotters surrounded the palace. The appointed assassins, dressed in military uniforms, were about to enter the building when one of the organisers, in fact the brains behind the whole plot, changed his mind. He ordered his men to seal the palace to protect the King. Do you know who that was?' he asked. 'That political chameleon, Colonel Damyan Velchev.'

Velchev commanded the unwavering loyalty of a large swathe of ordinary officers. We had no idea why he had such a following. Some said that it was his sense of justice, others his dark charisma. He had already masterminded one *coup d'état* back in 1923 when the democratically elected Stambuliiski was deposed and killed. I can tell you from experience that he had tremendous presence. I met him once. It was an early winter's evening and I was late for a student meeting. I ran to catch the tram. Turning the corner behind the military club, I saw a man in front of me. I tried to stop but it was too late. I fell into his arms. He held me by the shoulders. I looked up. He wore a military cape, a sword hanging on his belt. The face was dark and scarred, and my shoulders trembled. His eyes were shadowed by the peak of his military hat, but I recognised Damyan Velchev. He squeezed my shoulders and said nothing. I can still remember the touch of those big leather gloves. Ten years later, this avowed anti-monarchist would play a leading role in another military coup of historic proportions.

I looked at Alexander's face, flushed with excitement from what he had heard at Nissim's house. His eyes were burning again. I hadn't seen him like that for a long time.

'And do you know what?' he asked. 'Listen to this: they're going to establish diplomatic links with Moscow. Can you believe it?'

Nissim Mevorah was very well connected, and there was no reason to think that what Alexander had just learned was untrue. As it turned out, the plotters didn't last very long. They clung on to power for about a year, but they did at least establish diplomatic links with Soviet Russia. King Boris III, the son of 'Foxy' Ferdinand Saxe-Coburg, eventually outmanoeuvred them. Without any violence, Kimon Georgiev, the anti-monarchist war hero from the Great War, was forced to resign, though his life was spared. The monarch assumed absolute power without being an absolute monarch. Diplomatic links with Moscow were kept open for a number of years until Bulgaria reluctantly joined the Axis in 1941. But until his last days Boris III would be mindful of his nation's historic ties with Russia. He would even defy Hitler in that respect and refuse to send Bulgarian troops to serve on the Eastern Front.

During the short reign of the plotters, Alexander made his first trip to Moscow. Very few people know about this. Some even say it didn't happen, but I know that Alexander went to Moscow in 1935. The visit was organised by the Comintern after its seventh, and last, congress. Apparently, Dimitrov personally identified the three men from Bulgaria chosen to visit Soviet Russia and meet Stalin.

The journey was shrouded in secrecy. Alexander and his two comrades from the Bulgarian Communist Party first travelled to Berlin. In the German capital they were met by Comintern operatives who put them on the train to Warsaw. From there, they took another long train journey to Moscow. That was the approved channel managed by the Soviet NKVD, predecessor to the KGB. Many Soviet agents and foreign communists travelled to Moscow using that pipeline.

The other two men chosen by Dimitrov for this special journey did not return.

7

10 September 1963

'HAVE YOU BEEN TAKING YOUR MEDICATION?' MAJOR Ohridski asked.

Alexander Ivanov looked sleepy and dishevelled, his eyes vacant. The interrogation room was brightly lit. This time there were two more people behind the desk. Major Ohridski was sitting in the middle, even though the other two outranked him: a colonel and a lieutenant-colonel.

'Have you got me out of bed to ask me about my medication?' asked Alexander grumpily.

'We would like to know if you're being properly looked after,' the major said with a serious voice, ignoring the sarcasm of the accused.

'Yes, I have my medication now.'

'Very good. Does the food we give you meet your dietary requirements?'

'No, but I try to eat only small amounts.'

'So, you can't really complain about the way we look after you.'

'No, I can't. Actually, I expected to be held in a small dingy cell but the room I was given is very nice: large and bright. And the bed linen is very clean.'

'Good, good,' the major said complacently. 'Now you can start talking to us.'

'Talking about what?' There was unconcealed irritation in Alexander's voice.

'Well, when and where did a foreign intelligence agency approach you for the first time?'

The major did all the talking. The other two sat in silence.

'What agency are you talking about?' Alexander asked, and immediately changed the subject: 'Did your son enjoy the fireworks?' There was no reply, so he continued: 'There must have been a real sense of occasion. It's the nineteenth anniversary of our Bulgarian socialist revolution. And who would've thought that the dwarves would've climbed to the top...'

'What do you mean by that?' the colonel, who had so far kept his silence, interjected.

'I mean that the cowards who went into hiding during the underground struggle against the fascist regime are now running the country. After the Red Army put us in power, they killed their rivals on trumped-up charges and triumphed to the top. In American corporate culture this is called "punishment of the innocent and reward of the non-participants".'

All three members of the interrogation panel looked at each other with some anxiety.

'We shall come to that subject later,' the colonel said. 'Now back to the business in hand. When did the American CIA first approach you?'

'You've got no evidence whatsoever, have you? That's why you are trying to make me confess to something I haven't done.'

'Look, you will be interrogated day and night until you tell us everything,' Major Ohridski said sternly. 'It's in your interest to stop behaving like a petulant child and start taking responsibility for what you've done.'

'I haven't done anything. Are you going to torture me to extract a confession?'

'No, we don't do torture,' the major said with an ironic smile on his face. 'But there are things far worse than physical torture.'

After a couple of hours going around in circles they all got tired. Suddenly Alexander said, 'Why did you arrest me in Moscow and not here, in Sofia? I was due to come back here today, or yesterday. I've lost track of the dates.'

'This is our business and we don't have to answer your questions,' the major replied.

'Of course,' Alexander said compliantly. 'And something else: when can I see my wife? I am worried about her. She must be living in terrible fear. The fear will kill her. She will die because of you.'

'Well, start talking and you will see her. For example, did you have any private conversations with American diplomats when you were in New York?'

'Of course I did. It was my job to talk to all sorts of diplomats. We regularly discussed international affairs.'

'And did you inform our foreign minister of these discussions?'

'Oh my God!' Alexander exclaimed. 'You haven't got a clue, have you? The foreign minister, Karlo Lukanov, is an idiot; our ambassador in Washington is an arsehole; and Tarabanov, our head of mission at the UN, who I've known for a long time, is an enemy. Who did you want me to inform? They wouldn't listen. The whole foreign ministry is full of fuckwits. And Zhivkov is not interested in the truth. He's got his own secrets...'

'That's enough for tonight!' the colonel interrupted him abruptly and switched off the recording machine. It was 1.45 a.m. The guard took Alexander back to his solitary cell. The three interrogators looked worried.

At the same time, a few miles away from the State Security Directorate where Alexander was being held, another meeting was taking place. After the official banquet to celebrate the anniversary of the communist takeover, three people gathered in a small room on the top floor of the Palace of Vrana, a former hunting lodge of 'Foxy' Ferdinand's, now an official residence of the country's new leaders. The three had waited for the black limousines to ferry the members of the politburo and their families away. One of them was Todor Zhivkov, first secretary of the Central Committee of the Communist Party and prime minister; the second was Ivan Yazov, Head of Counterintelligence at the Committee for State Security, known as Zhivkov's loyal hitman; the third person was a short but well-built middle-aged man with grey hair, who was not known to the chief of the palace security. He had arrived at the palace in a black Chaika limousine with Soviet diplomatic plates. The car belonged to the political section of the embassy.

It is not possible to find out what exactly was said at this meeting, but it sealed Alexander Ivanov's fate.

8

DORA IVANOV

28 AUGUST 1943: THE KING IS DEAD, LONG LIVE THE KING!
The official announcement was brief, only a few words explaining
that King Boris III had died suddenly after a short illness. It took
everybody by surprise and the rumours started immediately.

Nissim Mevorah told us that the King had died a few hours after
returning from a hiking trip to Moussala, the highest mountain in
Bulgaria. He had a high temperature, his skin was covered in red
and brown blotches, and he was short of breath. All the symptoms
suggested that he had been poisoned. We later found out that this
information came from the King's private secretary. The official
announcement said that the monarch had died of a heart attack.
He was forty-nine.

King Boris III, son of Ferdinand Saxe-Coburg and Princess
Marie Louise of Bourbon-Parma, was a deeply flawed character.
On the one hand, he wanted to be loved by his people and did
everything possible to portray himself as the people's monarch.
Dressed in full combat uniform, Boris III stared into the distance
from the front cover of *Time* magazine in its issue of 20 January
1941. Bulgaria was then in the spotlight, with frantic speculation
about whether it would join the Tripartite Pact with Germany,
Italy and Japan. 'Boris of the Bulgars is an amiable man,' wrote
Time. 'He is a peace lover who likes to mount butterflies' wings
and study mountain petals, to step on automotive accelerators and
pull locomotive throttles.' He told *Time*: 'It would not frighten

me if I were to lose my throne. If that were to happen, I would go right to America and get a job as a mechanic.'

He regularly drove trains across Bulgaria and people flocked to see him in his blue overalls leaning out of the front window of the steam locomotive. Even in the happiest of times, his pale face looked pained. His black peasant moustache mitigated those sharp Bourbon features: the characteristic deep-set eyes and long curved nose on an almost completely bald head. That was Boris, the man.

On the other hand, Boris the politician was ruthless. Opponents who couldn't be corrupted with money and power were simply murdered. He was an old-fashioned king working all his life for the preservation of the monarchy and perpetuating the royal bloodline. This was paramount in every decision that he made, even when it looked as if compassion were the driving force. In July 1943, Churchill and Roosevelt finally carried out the landing of Allied Forces in Sicily. Mussolini was deposed and Italy came out of the war. At the same time, Stalin made a decisive push against Hitler in the Battle of Kursk, which became the graveyard of the German elite armoured divisions. Boris III was looking for a way out.

On 20 July 1943, a curious meeting took place in Sofia. I was asked to attend to a sick man at the house of the director of the Zoological Garden in Sofia, Professor Buresh. The professor's wife knew my family in Zagora and she had followed my career in medicine. When I arrived, I was surprised to see Georgi Gubidelnikov in the house, scion of the grandest Bulgarian banking dynasty. They were fabulously rich.

The hosts introduced the sick man as a Swedish businessman by the name of Carl Frist. He was lying on the couch in one of the guest bedrooms. He asked me if I spoke English, and I told him that I had spent a year and a half at St Mary's Hospital in Paddington, specialising in bacterial infections. He smiled but his face looked exhausted. I recognised that man, but I wasn't sure if I was supposed to tell him that. He said that he suffered from colitis, a chronic inflammation of the lower bowel, aggravated by stress, he added. And he had been under a great deal of stress recently. Then I overcame my timidity and said that I had seen him at some Unity Campaign demonstrations in London in 1936 when he was a leading figure in the anti-fascist left, advocating cooperation with the communists. I told him I had heard his speeches warning against the threat of fascism. He opposed the appeasement of Hitler. I said I'd agreed with him then, and that history had proven him right. His tired eyes smiled at me. This was Sir Stafford Cripps, a Labour politician who until the previous year had been the British ambassador in Moscow. I knew that this was no ordinary meeting.

I heard that Sir Stafford had come to Sofia with a proposal to persuade Bulgaria to withdraw from the Axis and come out of the war. The proposal, supported by the Gubidelnikov banking family, was simple: military officers were to stage a *coup d'état* similar to the one in 1934, ask the King to cooperate in return for keeping the monarchy, and declare neutrality. For their part, the Allied Forces would open a second front against Germany in neighbouring Greece. That was Churchill's preferred option. Allied troops would invade Bulgaria and that would guarantee that the country didn't fall under Stalin's boot.

Two weeks later we learned that Hitler had invited King Boris III to a meeting at the Wolfschanze (The Wolf's Lair), his military headquarters in Eastern Prussia. The King delayed his departure for a few days until the Führer grew impatient. King Boris knew what was expected of him, and despite the warnings from his closest advisors, he left Sofia by plane on 14 August. The visit was publicised by the German propaganda machine. The King was seen walking with Hitler in the grounds of a bunker in the Masurian Woods, in what was then Poland, discussing politics in front of big maps and drinking tea together. But neither of them looked happy. The strain on their faces was there for all to see.

The Bulgarian newspapers reported that the King had again categorically refused to send Bulgarian troops to the Eastern Front to fight the Russians. He had also rejected a request to send Bulgarian Jews to the death camps in Treblinka and Majdanek, in occupied Poland. This was the last Nazi effort in the long campaign to complete the Final Solution. German steam barges were waiting on the Danube to take their cargo away. But the King stood his ground. What Boris III couldn't do was to save more than 11,000 Jews from the annexed territories of northern Greece and Yugoslavia. These territories, although given to Bulgaria as a reward for being in the Axis, were jointly occupied by Bulgarian and German troops. The Jews were deported by the Germans and most of them perished. But 50,000 Bulgarian Jews were saved.

On the day when the King's death was announced, we had a sense of foreboding. The outpouring of grief was overwhelming. Hundreds of thousands of ordinary citizens passed by his body lying in state at the golden-domed orthodox cathedral of Alexander Nevski in the centre of Sofia. There was genuine sadness on people's faces as they queued up to bid a final farewell to him. Alexander and I didn't go.

Rumours persisted that the King had been poisoned by Hitler. His six-year-old son, Simeon, was proclaimed king under a Regency Council headed by Kiril, Boris's younger brother.

My message about Sir Stafford's visit to Sofia was duly passed to Soviet intelligence through our illegal communication channels with Moscow. We hoped that the Red Army would be here soon. We just had to survive for a little bit longer.

But Alexander's work was getting steadily more dangerous. He helped bring weapons from Stalin to the Bulgarian armed resistance. Alexander would be passed a coded message received by someone else from a radio transmission. He would decode the message and organise the partisans to pick up the airdrop at the agreed time and place. There was also money. Illegal airdrops of cash – mainly German Reichsmarks but also dollars and Swiss francs – were delivered to the capital by trusted couriers. Alexander was once stopped by the police outside the Church of the Seventh-day Adventists in Solunska Street in Sofia with a suitcase full of German marks for the party. He blagged his way out but was pretty shaken afterwards.

Although he already had his own legal practice, he still worked closely with Nissim Mevorah. Nissim's house was the focal point of the proletarian intelligentsia in Bulgaria. Well-known writers, artists and actors, many of whom were not even members of the banned Communist Party, gathered there for discussions. They also went to hear the latest news from Moscow.

A few months before the King's death, Alexander was called for questioning by the police. Although he wasn't arrested, they kept him there for a whole day. For the first time he came face to face with the notorious Head of Department 'A' of the Police Directorate, Nikola Geshev, the man in charge of fighting the communist resistance in Bulgaria. Alexander was never the same after this encounter.

Alexander was very good at building psychological profiles of people, something that he had learned at the Sorbonne in Paris to help him in court. He saw Geshev as a recluse and a frustrated writer. He identified him as a sociopath with a deep inferiority complex. Geshev was very bitter about not having achieved a university degree. He felt it necessary to tell Alexander that he had studied law in Italy for two years but lacked the money to continue his education. He was well informed about philosophy, Marxism and Stalinism. Geshev would frequently leave the interrogation room, and Alexander was certain that he was being observed when left alone. They ordered a good meal for him with half a bottle of his favourite red wine.

Geshev was up to speed about what was going on in the Soviet Union. But what shocked Alexander most was that he was privy to really intimate details of our private lives. He used this information sparingly, without boasting. He told him that he knew about Alexander's visit to Moscow in 1935. He said that Alexander was very wise to have returned to Bulgaria at the time because if he hadn't, like his two companions, he would have died in Stalin's Gulags. He also mentioned the 'submariners' and the 'parachutists': armed Bulgarian expats sent by Moscow to Bulgaria in 1942 to instigate an armed resistance against the regime. Alexander knew some of them. They were arrested and executed. The police knew where to find them as if they were expecting them. These arrests incapacitated Stalin's efforts to create a large-scale communist movement in Bulgaria. Geshev implied that this was possible because he had a mole or even several moles in the highest echelons of the Communist Party. He knew everybody on the party central committee by name and rank. The most shocking revelations came at the end of the day when Alexander was very tired.

'I know that Germany is losing the war,' Geshev fired the first salvo. 'It's only a matter of time before the Soviet troops come knocking on our door.'

At the time, anyone who voiced something remotely close to such an opinion would be tried for treason and executed. But Geshev was very calm and assured in his invulnerability. It wasn't immediately clear if this was a genuine statement or something designed to entice Alexander to open up. But there was more to come: 'The King will not survive his confrontation with Hitler. He will abdicate or die before the war is over. Your party will rule Bulgaria for decades to come. The question is, do you fight us now and get killed, or do you cooperate with us and stay alive? This is not just an existential question in the philosophical sense. It is a very practical question. Which of your party colleagues do you want to eliminate now in order to clear the board of any competition in the future? Some in your ranks have already made up their mind. They cooperate with me to stay alive. And they give me names, addresses, action plans. You can't believe how eager some of your friends are.'

Alexander said that he tried to keep his composure but was shaken to the core. Even if this man was lying, one could see a certain pattern in the recent trials. Some of the accused in the so-called trial of the members of the Central Committee last year were sent to jail, others executed. One name sprang to mind – Traicho Kostoff, one of the most able leaders the party had had. The official version was that his life was spared by the King after a plea from his private secretary, who was an old school friend of Kostoff's. What Alexander didn't know was that in the same class in the same year there was another bright boy, a scholarship boy, whose life had taken a different path: Geshev himself.

'I have followed your work as a defence lawyer very closely,' said Geshev. 'You have had a high success rate in saving people from the gallows. I can make life much easier for you. If you need to save anybody in the future, just call me. I can make that happen. You and I can have a very productive relationship.'

At the end of the long day, Geshev accompanied Alexander from his office, chatting away to him as if they were old friends. At that moment, they bumped into one of the Communist Party activists strolling casually in the corridors of the Police Directorate. The two looked at each other but didn't say a word. In Alexander's opinion, Geshev was such a brilliant policeman that this encounter could not have been an accident. Alexander didn't tell me who that man was. He only said he was a printer he'd seen occasionally at secret party meetings.

9

21 SEPTEMBER 1963

'CAN YOU TELL ME ABOUT YOUR RELATIONSHIP WITH DR Tonka Karabasheva?' Major Ohridski said, beginning the interrogation session.

'We were lovers. It was November 1944, I think, when we began our affair,' Alexander said matter-of-factly.

'And how long did this affair last?'

'We still see each other, well, until I was arrested. But I was going to end it.'

'Well, well,' the major said smugly. 'She says that you promised to leave your wife and start a new life with her. But she grew tired of your prevarications and voluntarily came to us to denounce you as an American spy.'

'What can I say,' Alexander said wryly. 'Women. They are unpredictable. Have you ever had an affair, Major Ohridski? No? You don't know what you are missing. The fear of being found out is exhilarating. You get butterflies in your stomach like a teenage boy. It keeps one young forever. I recommend it.'

'Is it true that she came to visit you in New York when you were working at the UN?'

That caught Alexander off guard. He paused. The major knew that he had scored another point.

'She might've come to New York but not to visit me. For several years she worked at the Institut Pasteur in Paris. I tried to get her a visa for America but I couldn't.'

'How about the other women in your life? Did you treat them in the same way?'

'Hmm, there is only one woman in my life and that's my wife, Dora. The others are just lovers, mistresses.'

'But you are separated now? No? She doesn't live in your new apartment. She has moved out, hasn't she? It's a pity because I have to say the apartment has been furnished to a very high standard, I would say a Western standard. Not like mine.'

Alexander didn't answer. They sat in silence for a few seconds.

'Is Madame Bovren your mistress, too? And the young girl in our Paris embassy whose job was to decode the secret telegrams? And Rosa Aronova, your secretary at the embassy at the time? And the woman in Zagora who you got pregnant as a student? And Olga from Moscow? How many more mistresses have you got?'

'Am I here for bad behaviour, or what? Are you the moral police?'

'Your wife will be the judge of your behaviour. She hasn't been arrested,' the major said triumphantly. 'She is very well, indeed. In fact, she is here now, listening to our conversation.'

'Oh, that is a very pleasant surprise. Would I be allowed to see her?' Alexander's face lit up.

'Of course, but before that somebody else wants to have a conversation with you.' The major switched off the recording machine.

Alexander was left alone in the room a good half hour. When the door finally opened he saw a middle-aged man, grey-haired, blue-eyed and well-built. Seemingly a man like any other. But as he entered Alexander felt a cold wind sweeping the room. He looked to the window, but it was closed fast. If he had been a believer, he would have said that the devil himself had flown through the metal bars of the state security interrogation room and was now standing right behind him.

The man was dressed in an expensive black suit, as ever a marker of a privileged position in the hierarchy. He sat at the desk and smiled at Alexander. There was something familiar in his face.

'We met many years ago in Moscow,' the man said in Russian. 'It was 1935. We attended the same NKVD course. We were taught the art of subversive activities.'

Alexander cringed at his pomposity. Yes, at the time they were taught how to organise uprisings, revolts and revolutions, how to sustain guerrilla warfare, and the skill of political assassinations. But, most importantly, the young cadets on that short course were told that they had to be prepared for total sacrifice for the cause of communism and Stalin. They had to be prepared not only to lay down their lives for the great leader and the struggle for world communism, but also the lives of the people they loved.

'I won't pretend this is going to be easy,' the man said. 'You are an intelligent man and you will understand our position.' There was a deliberate and well-timed pause. 'We both know that you have spied for the CIA,' the man continued, with chilling precision. 'We have the evidence. You have been under total surveillance since May this year. We have read your letters, even those signed George Duvall, we've listened to your phone calls, and we've identified the people you have met. We know about things that you've done, which even you don't know. No, that's not a joke. It's not an attempt to frame you, either. And it's not a thing that we want to come out in the trial. Apart from passing classified information to the CIA, you are responsible for the death of one of our agents in the United States. He was a high-value asset. We tracked down the leak to the Bulgarian embassy in Washington at the time when you were temporarily in charge of the legation safe. Does that ring a bell?'

Alexander shot a glance up into the man's face. He wore a pleasant smile.

'But as you well know,' the man continued, 'we don't need any evidence to have you killed. You can die in a car crash, or fall down from the window of your sixth-floor apartment…'

Alexander bit his lip. He knew that all these things were very real. At any moment, he could meet with one of those unfortunate accidents. He had even thought that he might be poisoned in a hotel room during his travels.

'During the Great Patriotic War I worked for SMERSH. I don't have to spell it out to you what this organisation, most secretive and most loyal to Stalin, did. It killed spies. Stalin personally invented the name for the organisation. In the war, there was no time for lengthy investigations, trials and all those legal niceties. The arrest and execution of anybody accused of spying for the Germans had to be approved only by their direct superior. Then they got a bullet in the back of the head, execution style. We carved a sign on their foreheads with a knife. Behind enemy lines in Ukraine, we used to burn them alive tied to a stake. The screams haunted the countryside. People said they used to hear phantom screams long after the charred bodies had been taken down. In the cities, we took the spies to railway stations and threw them alive into the burners of the steam engines on the platform. We wanted all to know what happens to those who betray our motherland.'

Alexander's gaze was fixed on the man's forehead, avoiding his eyes.

'We told you at the Lubyanka after your arrest that you may become useful to us. Our Bulgarian comrades will tell you what to do to expose the American spies in your country. But after that we want a trial. We want you to confess in court. We want every single detail of your work for the CIA out in the open. We want the Americans exposed and humiliated. If you cooperate in our propaganda war, your life will be spared. You will be given a new identity.'

Alexander bit his lip again. At that moment, he knew the game was up. There was no guarantee that this man would keep his word. And who was he, anyway? Some mid-level apparatchik in the Political Directorate of the KGB? He would confess, but only on his terms. Now was the time to bargain.

'Sure, I'll cooperate,' Alexander said slowly. 'But I want one single thing in return. I don't ask for my life. That's far too cheap.'

The other man looked at him in anticipation.

'It's my wife, Dora. She has absolutely no involvement in what I've done, and I ask you to leave her alone. She is a good woman, a hard worker all her life. She has a wonderful career in science. She has a lot to give. Don't ruin her life.' Alexander felt a tear swelling from his eye and looked aside to conceal it from the man.

'I shall pass your request to the head of the KGB but personally I don't think that this should be a problem. It all depends on your cooperation.'

No sooner had the KGB man left the room than Dora appeared at the door. They embraced. Alexander put his finger on her lips and whispered in her ear: 'Don't worry. Everything will be fine.'

They stood in an embrace in the middle of the room – two short middle-aged people holding each other tightly. Dora's head nestled on Alexander's shoulder, her ear firmly pressed to his chest as if listening to his heartbeat. He had buried his face in her hair. They didn't have to talk. They could read each other's minds.

Major Ohridski felt uncomfortable looking at the couple. They both seemed quite ordinary, and he was suddenly reminded of his parents. But he felt cheated. The battle of the wills between him and Alexander was over. The man was broken and he would now confess. Of course, he was excited by the prospect of learning the finer details of Alexander's spy work, the means of communication and the people behind it. But the major wanted more. He wanted to understand the man and what had motivated him.

10

DORA IVANOV

ON 9 SEPTEMBER 1944, THE RED ARMY INVADED BULGARIA. The Russians occupied north-eastern Bulgaria and the Black Sea ports. During the night, the same group of officers who staged the *coup d'état* in 1934 seized power in Sofia again. Using the same blueprint, the tank regiment based on the outskirts of Sofia and a motorised division stationed in a neighbouring town occupied the main military and propaganda installations in the capital. Retired Lieutenant Colonel Kimon Georgiev, the same man who led the *coup d'état* ten years earlier, was once again declared prime minister. His friend and fellow coup leader from 1934, General Damyan Velchev, became defence minister. Neither was a communist. They had joined the Fatherland Front the previous year. The Fatherland Front was a broad anti-fascist coalition created by the communist leaders in exile, Dimitrov and Kolarov, with Stalin's blessing. The Communist Party was joined by a wing of the Agrarian Union, the Social Democrats, the anti-monarchist officers' group (Zveno), and some independent high-profile individuals with republican and anti-fascist views.

The radio announcement in the morning said that the Fatherland Front had seized power in a bloodless coup, Bulgaria had declared war on Nazi Germany, and a new Regency Council had been appointed to administer the state on behalf of the seven-year-old King Simeon II, son of Boris III. The royal family was placed under house arrest at the Palace of Vrana.

Alexander and I didn't know what to do. He was getting anxious because no one from the Communist Party had told us what to expect and we had to learn about the coup from the radio. There hadn't been any message from the Central Committee about what was expected of him. We had waited for this for such a long time, and when the day finally dawned we felt left out. Although things were moving fast, as members of the Fatherland Front we expected to be involved in some way. But there was an ominous silence. Other people were already taking up key positions in the new administration.

After midday, Alexander walked down the street to the house of Nissim Mevorah. He was not at home. His wife told him that Nissim had been taken to the War Ministry where the new Council of Ministers was based. The main building of the Cabinet Office was damaged in the aerial bombardments by Allied aircraft during the war and the Cabinet was evacuated to the small village of Pancharevo outside Sofia, on the way to the Rila Mountains. Now that the war was over for Bulgaria, the new Cabinet was sitting in the War Ministry building. They were drawing up letters to the Allied powers about Bulgaria's new status as a country at war with Germany. The communists, she said, would insist that the new government issued a decree for the establishment of a National Guard and People's Militia, which were to take control of internal security. Alexander was despondent. Things were happening without him. When he came back home he looked abandoned and lonely.

The telephone lines had been cut off. The post office had been shut down. People were told to stay indoors. I sneaked out of the house and walked down the street to an old friend from the Student Union who lived in the same neighbourhood. She said that the new government now communicated between the ministries only by messengers. No written orders. Only verbal messages.

She said that the place to go was a hotel in the centre of Sofia, Slavyanska Beseda, which was being set up as the headquarters of the newly formed People's Militia. There was no decree for the establishment of the militia yet, but our comrades were arming themselves and had started to round up all the fascist ministers and collaborators. If you wanted to take part in the new workers' power in the country, go to the hotel. You would get weapons, ammunition and you would be assigned a task. That hurt Alexander even more. He was getting paranoid. Why was he excluded? His pride was dented.

After agonising about whether to go or not, he decided to walk down to the hotel. There was no public transport, so it took him half an hour to reach the city centre. The hotel was a stylish 1930s building within a short walk of the royal palace and the War Ministry. It was early evening when he approached. The usually grey limestone facade glowed golden under the fading sunset. But when he tried to go through the glass double doors of the hotel he was stopped by two rough-looking unshaved men in peasant clothes with red armbands tied above their left elbows. They were carrying German Karabiner rifles on their shoulders, and German Mauser pistols were tucked into their sweat-stained leather belts. Their clothes smelled of dust and damp.

'Who do you want to see, comrade?' the younger one challenged.

Alexander didn't know what to say. He wanted to say that he was keen to get involved in the building of the new communist state, that he was a communist and a lawyer, that he had been to Moscow and had met Stalin, but there was a lump in his throat. His pride prevented him from explaining all that to these peasants with guns. He was angry. He managed to utter the first words that came to his mind: 'I wanted to see Catherine Avramova. Is she here?'

'Actually, she was here this morning but she has gone now.'

Catherine was a good friend from the struggle. She was the link between him and the Party Central Committee when he was looking after the shipments of weapons from Moscow to the guerrillas in the mountains. So, she was already involved.

As he was about to leave, the doors opened and the two guards in peasant clothes saluted. A youngish medium-built man with sharp features and thinning hair, wearing a black woollen suit, white shirt and no tie, rushed out of the building followed by two bodyguards in similar clothes. The man didn't spare a glance for Alexander but jumped into an open-top German Kübelwagen, obviously confiscated from the War Ministry, which was waiting outside the hotel. Alexander froze. It was the same man, the print worker he'd seen strolling about inside the Police Directorate the previous year when the Head of Department 'A', Nikola Geshev, gave him a lesson in predicting the future. Alexander shut his eyes. Where was Geshev? Had he been arrested? What had happened to his secret archive and the names of the police informants? He wanted to shout in despair.

It was a balmy September evening. Sofia was plunged into darkness; the organisers of the coup had turned off the power across the city. Despite that and despite the contours of some ugly ruins against the purple sky – a legacy of the destructive force of British and American aircraft – Sofia was as beautiful as ever. Alexander inhaled the fresh evening air as he approached his house through the Boris Garden. His anger had turned to sadness. A candle flickered in the ground-floor window of the house. I was waiting for him as I always did. When he saw my silhouette in the darkness of the hallway he sighed heavily and said, 'The revolution is happening without us.'

~

The next day there was a loud and urgent knock on the front door. We looked at each other, then Alexander peered cautiously through the curtains of the front room and saw a German Kübelwagen outside the house. The engine was running and the driver had his hands on the wheel. He had on a black flat cap and a red band circled his left arm.

'Comrade Ivanov?' said the voice of a young man.

'Yes,' answered Alexander.

He was standing face to face with the young man, almost a boy, who was dressed in a shabby school uniform, which he had outgrown many years ago.

'I have a message for you from comrade Catherine Avramova. You are wanted at the Interior Ministry immediately. I have orders to take you there.'

If the young man's voice hadn't been so friendly, this whole business would've seemed very ominous. Alexander swiftly threw a glance towards the military jeep in the street. The driver was looking at them with urgency as though he had other more important tasks to carry out and this was only a diversion.

'Let me get my coat and I'll be out in a minute,' Alexander said and went inside, leaving the front door open.

The young man didn't move. He obviously had instructions not to leave the house without Alexander. Ten minutes later, the Kübelwagen pulled up at the back entrance of the Interior Ministry, another large 1930s building with a limestone facade. Inside, the place was buzzing. There were lots of people coming and going, some of them wearing red bands on their arms. Some carried rifles on their shoulders, others had pistols in their belts.

'Alexander, my dear friend,' Catherine shouted with excitement, shaking his hand enthusiastically. 'It's a momentous day. The party is in charge of the Interior Ministry. Damyan Velchev from Zveno has taken the War Ministry. But Yugov has been appointed interior minister. He is not here yet. We don't know where he is. But I thought that we could do with you here. You are a lawyer and a trusted friend.'

'I shall be honoured to serve the country,' Alexander answered with a big smile on his face. 'Have you seen Nissim?' he asked.

'No, but I think he is at the Cabinet Office working with Traicho Kostoff on important draft legislation. They have been asked by Dimitrov to set up the People's Courts. The fascist butchers will have to face the people and answer for their crimes. The people want justice but there will be an Allied Control Commission with the English and the Americans to supervise what is going on here, so we have been warned against executions without trial.'

And so began Alexander's new career under the communist regime.

Anton Yugov turned up at the ministry the following day and immediately appointed Alexander as chief secretary. He became in effect a compliance officer. He had to justify in law the Red Terror that ensued. Catherine dealt with the administration.

Kostoff, the home-grown party leader, whose life had been spared by the late King in the 1942 trials, was released from prison on 6 September. No one knew where he'd been during the following two days, but he turned up in Sofia on 9 September and assumed the unofficial position of communist leader. Despite opposition from the actual coup organisers, Prime Minister Kimon Georgiev and War Minister Damyan Velchev (both non-communist members of the new cabinet), Kostoff had – unofficially – already put into motion the terrible purges aimed at the old regime. Gangs of armed communists and communist sympathisers roamed the streets of every single town and village of the country, rounding up members of the former power structures – local mayors, police and army officers, and tax officials. Wealthy landowners and industrialists with links to the Germans were also taken in. Local party leaders had been given a free hand to arrest and execute anybody they didn't like. The message from Dimitrov in Moscow was to instil fear in the population so that it didn't rise against the new government. The time for settling old scores had come. It was incredible to watch how many people took advantage and willingly participated in the killing and imprisonment of fellow countrymen, sometimes on the flimsiest of evidence or, in many cases, with no evidence at all.

Kostoff was a highly educated man; he understood the philosophy of revolution. His working life had begun as a stenographer in parliament, and he knew the names and faces of all the politicians from those times. On the evening of 9 September there was a stand-off between him and the war minister, Velchev. Kostoff wanted to have the whole royal family executed in the style of the Bolshevik revolution of 1917. Velchev, a committed anti-royalist himself, again refused to let the execution squad into the palace. He had done the same during the coup ten years earlier. A couple of days later, Dimitrov sent a telegram from Moscow ordering Kostoff to keep away from the royals. That was Stalin's wish. The only royal arrested was the old King's brother, Prince Kiril, simply because he had a political role as one of the three regents after the death of Boris III. There was something unnerving about him. Dark rumours circulated about his sex life. He wasn't liked in the way the nation liked his brother, King Boris. He was taken together with the other two members of the Regency Council and a great number of former government ministers – four cabinets in all stretching back to 1938. These orders came from Stalin.

Yugov was a simple, uneducated man. Hardened by the underground struggle, his vision was unobstructed by any moral argument. Kill or be killed was his philosophy. He was the de facto military leader of the communist guerrilla movement during the armed resistance. Alexander had met him in Moscow during his training in 1935. In the trial against the Communist Party in 1942, Yugov was sentenced to death in absentia. Physically strong, with big black hair and a moustache modelled on Stalin's, he was the perfect executioner. Stalin trusted him.

'I have a task for you,' he said to Alexander later. 'We have rounded up an awful lot of people and need to find a safe location to hold them.'

By the morning, Alexander had found a large compound in a working-class neighbourhood of Sofia known as The Stables (Konyovitza), north-west of the centre. It was close to the Interior Ministry and the Palais de Justice, where the People's Court was due to sit, and yet it was not easy to get to. Traditionally a communist stronghold, the population of the neighbourhood would provide a natural cordon sanitaire against intruders. The compound consisted of a single-storey building which housed a factory belonging to the National Union of the Blind. The large plot of land was fenced off with barbed wire. This would become the location that would haunt generations of Bulgarians. Very few people left that factory alive. Those who did were taken later to labour camps across the country.

Yugov was pleased with the location.

11

22 SEPTEMBER 1963

'GOOD MORNING, YOU LOOK VERY WELL TODAY,' MAJOR Ohridski said cheerfully.

Alexander didn't answer immediately. For the first time since the interrogation in Sofia had started, the major was dressed in full military uniform. His green peaked cap was sitting on the table by his right hand. Alexander noticed that the badge on the cap was almost indistinguishable from that of the Soviet KGB.

Dressed in a freshly ironed white shirt and his usual black suit, Alexander sighed heavily.

'Yes, I am well. Thank you for the daily portion of milk, which the guards have started to deliver to my cell.'

'Very well,' the major said briskly. 'Shall we start? I am inviting you to begin with a full confession about your work as an American spy.'

Alexander cleared his throat.

'Yes, I am an agent of the American CIA. My code name is George Duvall. I am also known under the names of Alexander Belov and Joseph Pachuta. I have travelled on Iranian, Iraqi and Syrian passports too.'

Major Ohridski took a deep breath. His excitement could not be concealed.

'Who chose your code name? You?' The major spoke more slowly than usual.

'The name George Duvall was chosen by my handler, George Anderson, who was my main contact at the CIA.'

'For the record, can you specify the names of *all* CIA operatives you have been in touch with up to the day of your arrest?'

'Anderson, Jackson, Bonar and Silence. There may have been others but I don't know their names.'

'Is Madame Bovren a CIA agent?'

'Yes, as far as I know she is, but I have had only a sexual relationship with her. I have never passed any classified information to Madame Bovren. She has never asked me to do so.'

'But Madame Bovren is twenty years older than you…' the major stuttered.

'So, what's that to do with anything you want to know professionally?' Alexander's voice firmed up. 'I think you should know that Madame Bovren comes from a very distinguished family of intellectuals. You'll have to be very careful how you handle any information concerning Madame Bovren because she and her family have a very cordial relationship with highly influential people in the Soviet Union. Be warned!'

The major coughed nervously. He knew that this investigation was a potential minefield. 'Tell me about George Anderson? What do you know about him?'

'Well, if you don't know who George Anderson is, your organisation should be closed down and everybody sacked for incompetence.'

'I am asking you to cooperate.' There was an undertone of anger in Major Ohridski's voice. 'Cooperate and explain for the record everything you know about George Anderson.'

'You probably know that George Anderson is the head of the CIA station in Istanbul. He is now based at the American consulate there and is responsible for the CIA activities in the Balkans. His real name is Cyril Black and his mother is Bulgarian…'

Cyril Black's father, Floyd, was the president of the American college in Samokov, an ancient town nestled in the foothills of Bulgaria's highest mountain range, the Rila. American missionaries from the Congregational Church had come to the Balkans in the second half of the nineteenth century to spread the gospel in what was then the Ottoman Empire. They set up a college in this secluded mountain town, away from the prying eyes of the Ottoman administrators, to educate young Bulgarian Christians. It thrived even after Bulgaria was given independence from the Ottoman Empire at the Congress of Berlin in 1878.

Dr Floyd H. Black arrived in Bulgaria in 1926. He came from Istanbul with his wealthy Bulgarian wife, who had received her education at the American college there, and their nine-year-old son, Cyril. Cyril, or Cy as he was affectionately known, was born in North Carolina.

Floyd Black was a skilful administrator. He sold the property in Samokov and with the proceeds and some donations from wealthy Americans, and a small grant from the Bulgarian parliament, built a fantastic new college in Simeonovo, in the outskirts of Sofia. Ironically, after the communist takeover, the college campus was turned into a training school for secret agents, the State Security Academy.

The family lived happily in Sofia for sixteen years until the US declared war on Bulgaria in 1942. Floyd Black moved back to Istanbul where he joined the OSS, the Office of Strategic Services, a wartime organisation created to coordinate espionage activities behind enemy lines. After the war, the OSS morphed into the CIA.

Cy Black was a precocious child. In the pre-war years, the family took extensive holidays in the Balkans and in Russia. By the time he was eighteen, Cy spoke Bulgarian, Russian, Greek and Turkish effortlessly. By 1945 Cy was already a professor of history at Princeton.

'I first met Cyril Black at a reception at the Foreign Ministry in Sofia in October 1945,' Alexander said slowly, enunciating every word carefully. 'He was part of an American mission sent by President Truman to evaluate the political situation in Bulgaria. The delegation was led by Mark Etheridge, a newspaperman from Mississippi. Naively, the Americans thought there was still a chance for Western-style democracy in Bulgaria. They still saw the Communist Party as a rag-tag bunch of bandits, incapable of holding on to power. Cy approached me with a glass of champagne in his hand. He was a lanky young man with blue eyes and blonde hair. I made a comment that he spoke Bulgarian like a native. He smiled and said, "Yes, because I am Bulgarian. Sort of, anyway. My mother is Bulgarian and I grew up here."

'I immediately knew that he was OSS, or CIA to be precise, as the new agency set up in September that year was called. He said that he and Etheridge had been to see General Biryuzov, the Soviet representative in Bulgaria. And... he smiled at me as if I were an accomplice... "Things are not looking good for American influence in Bulgaria," he whispered. He had read the situation correctly – Biryuzov controlled Bulgaria. Our poor country had replaced one foreign puppet master – Hitler's Gauleiter in Sofia, Adolf Beckerle – with another foreigner, Stalin's man in Bulgaria, General Sergey Biryuzov.'

'It's a fascinating interpretation of history,' Major Ohridski said. 'But we are digressing here. When did Cyril Black, or Anderson, first ask you to spy for the Americans?'

'Oh, it happened much later, but I was sure that during the three-week visit to Bulgaria in the autumn of 1945 Cy Black was scouting for potential recruits among the senior ranks of the Communist Party.'

12

OCTOBER 1963

From the Interior Ministry Archive

THE DETAINEE, ALEXANDER IVANOV, HAS AGREED TO PLAY
a double game. Our aim is to expose the CIA operatives in Bulgaria.
In the first instance, his home telephone number has been trans-
ferred to the prison cell. Incoming calls only. The first call he
received was from Madame Bovren in Paris. The conversation was
conducted in French. Madame Bovren hung up abruptly. There
was a suspicion that Alexander Ivanov had told her that he was
under arrest. The recording was verified by an approved translator
who confirmed that Ivanov had followed the instructions and had
not alerted Bovren to his detention. A second call from Bovren
two days later confirmed that she was not aware of his detention.
The operation continues...

During his interrogation, Ivanov gave us a telephone number
in Paris, which was to be used as an emergency contact with
George Anderson from the CIA. Our embassy in Paris checked
the number and it turned out to belong to the US embassy. One of
our intelligence operatives at the embassy called the number and
introduced himself as George Duvall. He asked for Anderson but
was told to ring back the following day. Our operative command
decided not to call this number again.

A letter written and signed by Alexander Ivanov was sent to
his handler, George Anderson, at an address in Lausanne. The
codename of the recipient was Madame Wagner. 'The Bulgarian

authorities have prevented me from going to the conference in Paris because of the non-participation of the Soviet lawyers. I am doubtful about the latter. They advised me to tell the organisers that I was indisposed. I am not sure if my trip to Geneva would be approved. Am very worried. Awaiting instructions.'

On 4 October 1963, a coded message was received on the frequencies found in Alexander Ivanov's home. Using the code card from his apartment our operatives decoded the following: 'What is the reason for writing to Lausanne? Did you personally telephone Robino or did you ask somebody else to call on your behalf? Madame Bovren has received your postcard from Moscow. We are very worried about you.'

On 8 October, Alexander Ivanov was asked to send a telegram to one of the emergency contact addresses in New York: 'Please advise the date of your departure.' According to Ivanov's confession this was the emergency signal notifying the CIA that he was in danger. The telegram was signed 'Mary'. This coded message was supposed to trigger Ivanov's extraction from Bulgaria...

Two days after the telegram was sent, Ivanov was taken out of his prison cell and made to drive his own Mercedes slowly along Moskovska Street awaiting George Blackwell's routine walk back from work at the American embassy. The car drove slowly past Blackwell but he pretended that he didn't see Ivanov and did not react...

18 October 1963. Our operatives received a coded radio message on Ivanov's frequencies: 'Telegram received. Preparing response. Wait on the corner of Ruski Boulevard and Benkovski Street at 18:00 on each of the following dates – 22, 23, 24 October. Wait there for 5 minutes only...'

22 October 1963. Operative command decided not to take Ivanov to the agreed place. George Blackwell left the embassy in a car with diplomatic plates. He drove slowly past the agreed

place but did not stop. Five minutes later, the head of American intelligence in Bulgaria, Houston, walked past the same spot. He stopped there for thirty seconds then looked at the window of the Polish art exhibition and left.

23 October 1963. George Blackwell and a representative of the Dutch airline KLM, Fontaine, met for a drink in the restaurant Berlin at 17:15. Ivanov was led to the agreed spot at 18:00. Blackwell and Fontaine arrived at the corner at 18:07 but Ivanov had already left because the agreed five minutes had passed...

24 October 1963. Ivanov was at the agreed spot at 18:00. Blackwell drove his car slowly towards Ivanov. The two made eye contact. Blackwell stopped the car. Two seconds later, he drove away without acknowledging his contact. We suspect that Ivanov had given him a secret warning...

Bulgarian State Security made one more effort to establish contact with the CIA on Alexander's behalf by sending a coded radio message on the same frequencies: 'Waited for three days but no one appeared'.

The CIA responded with a thinly disguised acknowledgement that Ivanov had been compromised: 'Message received. Your transmission schedule has been changed. Your new frequencies will be confirmed via Lausanne.'

That was the last message received from the CIA.

13

DORA IVANOV

I REMEMBER VERY WELL IT WAS 27 SEPTEMBER 1944 AND
Alexander didn't come home that night. He telephoned to say
that he had too much unfinished work. It was amazing that the
telephones were working again. He said that they were preparing
the lists of those who would be tried at the People's Court. Most
of them had already been arrested. It was important that those
responsible for the disastrous decision to join the war on the side
of Nazi Germany should be punished. Hitler's lackeys should be
tried for what they'd done. During the resistance years, captured
partisans had their heads severed and put on display in towns and
villages. Those who gave the orders and those who carried out such
butchery should be punished. But there were others. Dimitrov had
sent instructions from Moscow that the fascist intelligentsia must
be obliterated. The chilling message said that writers, journalists,
historians and anybody else who had justified the fascist ideology
in their work should be exterminated physically and ideologically.
Even those who had stayed neutral should be treated as an enemy
and needed to be re-educated until they proved their loyalty. We
were told that this was a revolutionary 'necessity', a term both
Lenin and Stalin frequently used.

But in the morning, the harsh reality of the revolution came
closer to home. Our neighbour Janet was in tears on our doorstep.
Her son had been arrested on trumped-up charges claiming he
was a member of a fascist group. She cried for help. I rang the

ministry and asked to speak to Alexander straight away. His secretary, Rosa, said that he was out with the minister. This couldn't wait and I jumped on the tram. Sofia was getting back to normal. Most of the shops were open, though there were fewer people on the streets. Food was still scarce but there were peasant women at the tram stops selling eggs and meat.

Rosa Aronova, Alexander's secretary, arranged for me to wait in a nice room and ordered coffee. God knows from where the ministry got these rare supplies. Rosa was a Jewish woman in her late twenties with black hair and plump hips. She had voluptuous breasts and sensuous pink lips. She was also very clever. She spoke fluent French and got things done. I knew that she and Alexander began an affair almost ten years earlier when, barely out of school, she was a secretary at Nissim Mevorah's legal practice at Phoenix Palace, an office building at the back of the royal palace.

When Alexander finally arrived, I told him with some urgency that Andrey, the son of our neighbour Janet, had been arrested. Somebody had denounced him as a member of the fascist youth group, Ratnik. They were an undercover organisation, and the names of the members were never made public – something like the Freemasons. But Andrey was a sweet and decent boy. He was twenty-four. He could never have been a member of this despised fascist group. Our neighbours weren't fascists. We knew them very well. They were honest, decent people. How could anything like that happen to their boy? Alexander had to do everything possible to get him back before it was too late.

Alexander looked at Rosa. She only nodded and said that she would get a car to take him to the factory in Konyovitza.

Alexander arrived at the factory by mid-afternoon. There was a crowd of a few hundred people outside the gates trying to find out what was happening with their relatives. There was fear and anguish rather than anger on the faces of these well-dressed middle-class people. Alexander's driver said to one of the guards that this was the chief secretary to the Interior Ministry, comrade Yugov's right-hand man, and that he was here to see the camp commander. A few minutes later the gates opened and the car drove towards the factory building.

The first thing that hit them when they entered was the stench of human excrement. The main factory floor had been cleared of all machinery and hundreds of frightened people, some of them semi-naked, were locked up there. The strong were still standing, the weaker lay on the cement floor. Alexander and his driver were led towards the office. They were asked to wait in a small room on the second floor overlooking the factory floor. Alexander stared at the wall. He didn't want to meet the eyes of all the people below looking to him for salvation.

The camp commander finally appeared. He was wearing a green military uniform without insignia. The epaulettes had been deliberately torn out. He was a short man of about forty with a broad unshaven face. His arms were strong and hairy. His dark hair was long and greasy. He looked like a partisan who had just come down from the mountains. His eyes were red and a distinct whiff of slivovitz hung about him.

'How can I help you, comrades?' he said in a loud voice, shaking their hands.

Alexander explained why he was there. He wanted to get Andrey out immediately.

'It may not be as easy as you think, comrade. The people detained here have not been properly identified yet. There are no lists, no photographs, no names.'

'Then you have to send one of your men to shout his name around until you find him. That's an order,' Alexander barked angrily. 'This man is innocent and I want to take him home with me now.'

'Is he a relative of yours?' The commander sounded puzzled by Alexander's request.

'It doesn't matter. I am telling you he is innocent and he shouldn't be here.'

'Nobody is innocent,' the commander murmured. 'They all claim they are innocent but if the wheel turns and you and I find ourselves down on the shop floor waiting to be executed there will be no mercy for us. There will be no mercy for us! Do you hear me? You can't trust the bourgeoisie.'

A shiver of disgust went down Alexander's spine. The place had been turned into a slaughterhouse on an industrial scale.

The commander gave the order to find Andrey. A couple of people in his retinue promptly disappeared down the stairs. He then turned to Alexander and his driver, and told them to wait.

They must've waited for about half an hour when two men in shabby woollen clothes brought Andrey into the room. He was pale and had dark rings under his eyes. His face was bruised. A few seconds later, the commander re-entered. He was followed by a short dark-skinned gypsy of indeterminate age who limped so badly that it was a wonder he'd made it up the stairs. This man had no shoes: his feet were wrapped in pig skin tied to his ankles with jute string. His face was scarred and he had lost almost all of his teeth. He smelled as if he lived in a sewer.

'Is that your man?' the commander asked, pointing at Andrey.

'Yes, this is him. Do you want me to sign any release papers?'

The commander smiled condescendingly. 'We don't do any paperwork here.'

He had hardly finished the sentence when the small gypsy man produced a piece of rubber hose from behind his back. Alexander knew what was about to happen but could only look helplessly on. The gypsy whacked Andrey on the calves with the length of black rubber. The boy screamed and fell on his knees. A second blow to his back threw Andrey face down on the floor at Alexander's feet. Satisfaction beamed on the gypsy's face as he looked down on the defenceless body. He gave two more lashes to the boy's legs, each time tearing into the flesh and opening a bloody wound through the torn material of the trousers.

'Mind the head!' said the commander sternly. 'His bourgeois mother will need to see his face.'

That seemed like an order for the gypsy to carry on with the senseless beating. Several more lashes of the heavy rubber hose fell on Andrey's legs and feet. The boy screamed in agony. At every blow the gypsy smiled toothlessly.

'Stop!' shouted Alexander. 'What the hell are you doing?'

'Teaching him a lesson,' the camp commander said. 'A small punishment for being a bourgeois mummy's boy. The bourgeoisie has to be taught a lesson. He will be able to walk again if mummy pays for a good surgeon but Hassan here is crippled for life. Look at him. Not only did they break his legs, the fascist police knocked his teeth out, too. And all that for stealing a loaf of bread. Now get this bourgeois scum out of here.'

The gypsy struck the boy again with all his strength across the calves. The crunching sound of broken bones pierced the air. Andrey lost consciousness. Alexander and his driver carried his bloodied body to the car.

14

27 OCTOBER 1963

ALEXANDER WAS LED INTO THE INTERROGATION ROOM BY two uniformed guards. Major Ohridski was leafing through a thick file on the desk without raising his eyes to acknowledge his arrival.

'Good morning,' he said finally, and closed the file.

'How long are we going to go on with this charade?' Alexander asked in a tired voice without answering the greeting. His hair had grown longer and his face looked very pale and wrinkled, as if he had aged in the last two weeks.

'Can I take you back to the first days after 9 September 1944?' the major said in a self-important voice. He was wearing an ill-fitting brown suit and a blue shirt. As far as his superiors were concerned he had done his job. Alexander had confessed to being an American spy. But now he had been asked to build a credible case for the prosecution so that when Alexander stood up in court there would be no last-minute surprises. 'You were appointed chief secretary to the Interior Ministry on 11 September 1944. How did that happen?'

'What has this got to do with my being an American spy? I have already told you I didn't become a spy until much later. It was, I think, in 1956.'

'But I would like to understand how this transformation occurred. The transformation from a committed communist who believed in the revolution to a renegade, spying for the enemy.'

Alexander shrugged his shoulders in contempt.

'Do you know that the Interior Ministry, in which you had such an important job, had actually opened a file on you in September 1944?' the major continued.

'I'm not surprised at all. Yugov kept files on everybody.'

'Are you not even a little bit curious to find out what name they gave you in your secret file?' The major paused, scanning Alexander's face. No reaction. The major continued: 'They called you the Unbeliever. Your comrades at the Interior Ministry reported that you were wavering, that you showed sympathy towards the bourgeois enemy. The file contains reports which say that you were weak, disorganised and obsessed with big philosophical themes rather than the work at hand. You see, people at the ministry didn't trust you then...'

'These were terrible times. No one trusted anyone,' Alexander said pensively. 'There was an intrinsic distrust among the grassroots of educated people like me. Many believed that because I studied in Paris and spoke foreign languages I was automatically untrustworthy. Peasants with guns only trusted other peasants with guns. It was difficult for intellectuals like me, and like Professor Nissim Mevorah for that matter. We had to prove our loyalty every step of the way. Those power-hungry uneducated people thought that building a better future could only be achieved through violence. Thousands of innocent people lost their lives in the first few years of the revolution.

'Do you know, Major Ohridski' – Alexander called his interrogator by name – 'my signature can be found on many death warrants but I can't say with my hand on my heart that all those people were guilty and deserved to die. Did you know that the People's Court issued 2,618 death sentences? I had to countersign each execution order. As a comparison, at the Nuremberg Trials only twelve people were sentenced to death.'

'Yes, your file mentions that you were very diligent and enthusiastic about carrying out the death sentences on all those convicted by the People's Court. But tell me, why did you put your neck on the line to save the life of a young man called Andrey?'

'Because my wife asked me to. You know, Dora and I are more than just husband and wife. We are friends, we are comrades, I trust her implicitly. We don't have children. We only have each other. How many children do you have, Major Ohridski?'

'Only one, a boy,' the major answered.

'Ah, yes, you told me, the boy you took to the fireworks last month. I've always thought that having children is very overrated. You put in a lot of effort raising them and you don't get very much in return. It's easy to have a child. It's not easy to make your child your friend. Taking your boy to see the fireworks is not going to be enough. If I may give you a piece of advice, make your son your friend. That will give you happiness in life. Nothing else.'

'The file says that the young man you saved went on to become an operative in the Interior Ministry.'

'It's ironic, isn't it? That's the only job I could arrange for him at the time. That was the only way to save him and his family from persecution. Yugov signed the order for his appointment. And that camp commander who ordered his legs to be broken committed suicide a few years later. He couldn't live with what he'd done to so many people. His wife said the screams of his victims haunted him at night. Those screams drove him to insanity. There is a moral somewhere in this story.'

'Can you tell me why in 1943 you terminated your membership of the Communist Party?' the major said, changing the subject again.

'This question only reveals how ignorant you are, my dear major. The party was banned. It operated underground. We didn't carry membership cards in our pockets, we didn't pay any subscriptions. I was given advice that if I wanted to see a communist future for our country I had only to survive, and I took it. I only told Nissim Mevorah that I wanted to distance myself for a while and he approved of it.'

'And who, may I ask, gave you such advice?'

'Well, major, you are now opening a whole new can of worms. You may regret ever asking me this question. I was taken for questioning at the Police Directorate in the summer of 1943. The notorious Nikola Geshev interrogated me. Brilliant policeman. *You* could learn a thing or two from him. He actually foresaw what was going to happen to the country and told me that if I kept my head down and survived for a year or two I would see the Red Army on our territory and the Communist Party in government.'

'And what did you have to do in return?' the major asked.

'As it happened, nothing. He left me alone. But something else happened while I was at the Police Directorate. I saw a man there, someone who also survived the persecution of the communists. Well, you don't really want to know his name. This will put you in a lot of trouble.'

'I want the truth. This is my job,' the major answered ambiguously.

'Well, the truth is that I saw our current leader, Todor Zhivkov, in the corridors of the viper's den. And he looked at home there. He behaved as if he knew his way around. Putting this on the record will create some difficulty for you, don't you think?'

'Our conversations are being recorded meticulously,' the major answered. 'I don't have the power to alter anything.'

'OK then. Just for the record, Andrey was not the only person I tried to save. I begged Yugov to spare the life of Dr Alexander Stanishev, a decent man and a brilliant surgeon. He found himself before the People's Court simply because in the summer of 1944, when the Soviet troops reached our borders, he joined an ill-fated and short-lived Cabinet as minister for the interior and health, or some such. He wasn't a fascist. On the contrary, that particular government in June 1944 consisted of people who actually wanted to sever links with Hitler. But Yugov said that his hands were tied. Dimitrov wanted everybody who'd been a member of any Cabinet since 1938 executed regardless of who they were. I went to see Stanishev in September 1944 just after his arrest. About a hundred people were detained in the cells of Sofia Central Prison. Can you imagine the spectacle of seeing all these powerful figures – former prime ministers, regents, courtiers and cabinet ministers – crammed into a crowded cell? Prime Ministers Filov and Bozhilov – they *were* fascists. Prince Kiril, the late King's brother and one of the regents, well, he was held in isolation. There were all those rumours about his fondness for young blonde soldiers, and that certainly didn't earn him any favours with the guards. All these people deserved to die. They brought the country to destruction. But Stanishev? No. He was a decent man.'

'I think that this will be enough for today,' the major said. He seemed a little bored.

15

Dora Ivanov

The Revolution came of age on 30 September 1944. The People's Court was born. The guilty would be tried by their peers. But there was some foreboding about how this was all going to end. Would the innocent die along with the guilty? The radio announcer read out a long list of people to be tried. Some on the list had already been killed without trial in the past three weeks.

There was a rumour doing the rounds that Prince Kiril had tried to commit suicide when the group of partisans – unshaven, in stinking clothes – burst into his palace bedroom. The prince clapped a pistol to his head and threatened to blow his brains out. But then he changed his mind and asked only if he could take his pyjamas with him. Unlike his brother, the late King, the prince was universally disliked. He could've been murdered there and then, but Stalin had ordered that the people who were at the helm over the previous ten years should be loaded on a plane and shipped to Moscow for interrogation before their trials started. This job was given to the Interior Ministry.

Alexander didn't have any doubts about the legality of the People's Court. He thought it was right and proper that those responsible for bringing Bulgaria into the war on the side of Nazi Germany should bear the consequences. And those responsible for hunting down and killing the anti-fascist communist guerrillas should be punished for their cruelty. Traicho Kostoff led the bloodbath. Yugov, too. In discussions, they often cited what happened in France after D-Day. In the three months after the Allied Forces invaded France in June 1944 until the liberation of the country was completed, followers of General de Gaulle had executed around 20,000 collaborators without any due process, just on the say so of their accusers. Those people were often denounced by other collaborators to conceal their own dirty secrets. Here, in Bulgaria, we had to be robust. We couldn't allow any fascist to escape justice even if they had denounced other fascists.

But the little-known print worker Alexander had spotted in the Police Directorate in the summer of 1943, didn't join the bloodthirsty revenge killings. He had an altogether different plan. Yugov had appointed him Chief Inspector of the uniformed People's Militia, with a rank of lieutenant colonel. From his base in the Slavyanska Beseda Hotel, he played his part in the Red Terror by carrying out industrial scale extortion from frightened wealthy residents of the capital. Witnesses whispered that they had seen piles of cash, gold and jewellery on the coffee tables in the lobby. Merchants and industrialists had been tortured, others threatened with the People's Court for collaborating with the Nazis, and they voluntarily parted with their wealth in the hope of saving their lives. No one knew where these riches disappeared to. Alexander was disgusted but he kept quiet. The revolution was happening and he was playing a big part in it. That was enough for him.

When he went to see Dr Stanishev in prison, his intention was to try to separate him from the group destined to be flown to Moscow. However, he found himself outranked by a Soviet colonel based at the prison. The colonel was in charge and he held the list of the one hundred most wanted political prisoners who Stalin had personally asked to be sent to Moscow. Stanishev's name was on that list. The doctor shrugged his shoulders and said,

'One can't escape one's fate. God will be my witness that I haven't done anything wrong.'

Alexander wanted to say that there was no God and that history was shaped by us, mortal humans, but he didn't. That was the last time he saw him. On their return from Moscow three months later, those people would be the first batch to be fed into the People's Court machine. The directive from Dimitrov was that no one should be acquitted. The death sentences were pronounced on 1 February 1945. A few hours later, in the dead of night, several military lorries took the convicted, handcuffed and shackled, to a bomb crater in the outskirts of Sofia. The first to be shot was Prince Kiril, such was the hatred of him. It was ironic that his death warrant was issued in the name of his nephew, the underage King Simeon II, who was still nominally the head of state. There was a rumour that he was killed with a bullet in the back of the head by a revolutionary poet, whose firebrand partisan poems became mandatory for generations of schoolchildren in the post-war years. This was disputed by historians. There were no records of who attended this mass execution. The poet himself committed suicide many years later, after the collapse of communism in Bulgaria.

Body after body fell into the crater. The last one to be shot with a bullet in the back of the head was Dr Alexander Stanishev. He had to certify the death of everybody before him so that, as a last gesture of mercy, no one was buried alive in the mass grave. Alexander thought of this as a historical necessity. A bright communist future awaited Bulgaria.

16

29 October 1963

'CAN WE BEGIN TODAY WITH A FULL ACCOUNT OF WHERE and when you were approached for the first time by Cyril Black? And how he persuaded you to become an American spy?' The major began the interrogation without even saying 'good morning' to the accused.

Alexander remained silent for a few seconds staring at the window, then cleared his throat. 'Well, the two didn't happen at the same time. What do I mean by that? By the summer of 1946, Yugov already knew that I was unhappy at the Interior Ministry. He often told me that I was a soft intellectual who didn't have the stomach for the unpleasant work that the revolution sometimes required. At the beginning of June, I was called by the prime minister, Kimon Georgiev. He was a matter-of-fact man; he didn't deal in lengthy conversations and went straight to the point...'

The war was over but the government couldn't start rebuilding the country until there was a peace treaty with the victorious powers, including the Soviet Union. The Allies had decided to convene a conference in Paris to work out the details of treaties with the minor Axis members: Romania, Hungary, Bulgaria and Finland. Greece and Yugoslavia, who fought against the Nazis and whose territories Bulgaria occupied with the help of Germany during the war, were demanding big chunks of Bulgarian territory and huge reparations. Bulgaria needed its best legal minds to fight our corner in Paris.

The conference started on 29 July 1946. Dora and Alexander arrived in Paris by train a few days in advance. The main delegation, which included the prime minister, Kimon Georgiev, and the de facto head of state, the chairman of the National Assembly, Vasil Kolarov, travelled by air. This was a daring endeavour because the only VIP aircraft the new government had at the time was a German-built transport plane with three engines, a Junkers Ju 52/3m. It had been re-conditioned and refurbished in a Bulgarian factory to carry eighteen passengers. Among the passengers was the Bulgarian soprano, Neli Karova, a renowned beauty. Her husband was the private secretary to the last fascist premier, Bogdan Filov. Karova's surprising metamorphosis from a beauty queen and the darling of the fascist regime to an art icon of the new Bulgaria was the subject of all sorts of sordid rumours. She was to take part in the gala concert at the opening of the peace conference.

Alexander was delighted to be in Paris again. The familiar smell from the sewers, the rundown houses with peeling facades, the throngs of people took him back to his student days. But things had changed. The people looked different – the women wore more revealing clothes, the shops were full of colour, there were more American cars in the streets. Paris was emerging from the austerity of war and was once again bursting with energy and style.

The provisional government of France, hosting the conference, had assigned accommodation for the Bulgarian delegation at Hotel Gare d'Orsay on the Left Bank, opposite the Louvre. Members of the delegation remarked that the hotel was unfashionable, rundown and the food was appalling. Alexander didn't mind staying in a fleapit. The location was perfect. He had lived nearby in the late 1920s and felt immediately at home.

There were big things to be discussed at the conference and he was proud to be at the centre of it all. In the grand surroundings of the Palais du Luxembourg, Kolarov made the opening speech on behalf of Bulgaria in perfect French. That impressed not only the hosts but the British and the American delegations. In the evening, Kolarov introduced Neli Karova to the glittering audience at the special concert. She received a standing ovation.

Both Kolarov and Georgiev were pleased with Alexander's abilities and they treated him as their equal. He had the demeanour of a seasoned international diplomat. He dressed well, his French was immaculate and he had an immediate grasp of the legal detail. He gained their confidence. Although he was just a legal advisor, a kind of secretary to the delegation, they treated him as a politician.

The Soviet delegation though was very suspicious of him. It was led by Molotov but he hardly spent any time in Paris. The man who ran the negotiations on behalf of Stalin was Andrey Vishinsky, who commanded Stalin's total confidence. As chief prosecutor during the purges in the Soviet Union before the war he had carried out Stalin's wishes ruthlessly and was responsible for the deaths of millions. It didn't escape the attention of the wartime leaders of the Allied powers that Vishinsky, in his capacity as deputy commissar of foreign affairs, had accompanied Stalin to the Yalta and Potsdam conferences, which had mapped out the post-war settlement. Addressing the Paris Peace Conference, he used the same infamous language deployed during the show trials of the 1930s. When he spoke in defence of Bulgaria's territorial integrity, he called the wartime regime in Bulgaria a 'band of criminals', 'lackeys of the Saxe-Coburg dynasty', and 'agents of German fascist imperialism' who pushed the 'noble Bulgarian people' into the war against their will. Privately, Stalin had given the Bulgarian government 'border guarantees', i.e. that he would resist any demands by the great powers to reduce Bulgaria's territory in size. Alexander was privy to all these secret discussions.

However, Stalin had an intrinsic distrust of anybody who had lived and worked in the West. By default, Alexander fell into this category. The Americans spotted their chance.

'One day during the conference,' Alexander continued, 'in the corridors of the Palais du Luxembourg where it took place, I noticed someone who I had met in Bulgaria before the war. His name was Angel Kuyumjiiski, but he told me he had changed his name to Angelo Cahan and was now an American citizen. He was wearing an American military uniform and had the rank of colonel.'

Angelo, a Jewish boy from Samokov, had graduated from the American college in the town before World War I and had subsequently built a business empire, which included banks, property and factories. After the military coup in 1934, he emigrated to Spain from where he continued to run his business empire. With the advance of Franco, he counted himself second time unlucky, and achieved another metamorphosis, this time by emigrating to America where he took American citizenship. Wearing an American uniform suggested that he, too, had become an agent for the nascent CIA.

While Angelo was explaining to Alexander that he was trying to retrieve his assets from Bulgaria before the peace treaty came into force, the two were joined by another mutual acquaintance, Cyril Black. Although Alexander and Cyril Black had met the previous year in Bulgaria, he introduced himself as George Anderson without any explanation. Angelo invited them both to his hotel. He casually mentioned that the food there was great and that they must sample the best that Paris had to offer. They accepted.

Angelo Cahan had taken a suite at Hotel de Crillon in Place de la Concorde, next door to the American embassy. The hotel was an imposing building with an impressive colonnade, a masterpiece of eighteenth-century French architecture. The grand interior was fit for kings and emperors. The post-war austerity stopped at the doors of Hotel de Crillon. Alexander hadn't tasted foie gras and fine French wine for a long time. The service was impeccable.

It was not clear to Alexander who paid for the lavish meal at the hotel's main restaurant – the CIA or Angelo himself. But it became clear that Angelo, despite representing the US Army, was also involved in a private capacity as a banker in purchasing wartime Bulgarian government bonds at a discount. His intention was to consolidate Bulgarian foreign debt and sell it back to the Bulgarian state after the peace treaty came into force. Alexander couldn't help but think that there was something vulgar in Angelo's business undertakings. Nonetheless, he enjoyed the hospitality of this Bulgarian-American millionaire.

George Anderson seemed more detached than before. He only wanted to know whether the leader of the anti-communist opposition in Bulgaria, Nikola Petkov, would stand any chance in the elections slated for later that year. Alexander said that, yes, Petkov would be elected to the new parliament, but his long-term future in Bulgaria didn't look good. He explained to Anderson that Bulgaria would be declared a republic after a referendum in September and that the royal family would be allowed to fade into exile unharmed. But the Western powers should be under no illusion that Bulgaria would escape its destiny as a communist country.

Then the conversation turned to French politics. They discussed the workings of the new provisional government and the personal qualities of its chairman, Georges Bidault. Angelo said that French politics would be messy for the foreseeable future. Alexander stunned his companions by his knowledge of internal French politics and his razor-sharp analysis. At the end of the conversation, he declared that France was a declining power and over the next ten years it would turn almost 'invisible', while a country like Yugoslavia would become a lot more influential on the international stage.

Before the sumptuous meal was over, Angelo made a proposal.

'He said to me quietly in English, in Anderson's presence' – here Alexander paused for a second – 'would I agree to work for the new American intelligence organisation, the CIA? As I didn't reply immediately, they took this as a possible "yes" and mentioned that they were prepared to pay me substantial amounts of money and explained how the money transfers would take place. They looked very disappointed when I declined. I said that I was a patriot and couldn't possibly betray my country, nor could I betray the cause of communism and Stalin. They were slightly unnerved by my response. They had thought that they had read me well. I saw them regularly over the following four years while I was based in Paris, but I gleaned more information from them than they from me.'

Major Ohridski listened in complete silence, transfixed by this tale of high politics and espionage. He was particularly interested in the story of Angelo Cahan. But Alexander now looked tired and the major decided to terminate the interrogation for the day.

17

Dora Ivanov

When, in July 1946, I heard that we were to move to Paris for the preparation and signing of the peace treaty, my heart was full of foreboding. I knew Alexander all too well. In pursuit of pleasure and intellectual challenge he was reckless. Paris could be his undoing. But on the other hand, I thought that it would be good for us to leave behind the bloodbath of the revolution, which had thrown our lives into turmoil. Also, I was looking forward to swapping the drabness of Sofia for the glamour of Paris. And I wasn't disappointed.

The Parisian summer hit us in the face. The drains at the hotel smelled. Food was scarce. But there was optimism in the air. 'La Vie en Rose' played on the radio all the time – we both loved Edith Piaf. The French Communist Party had emerged stronger after the war. The progressive forces were gaining the upper hand.

But this was also the Paris of intellectual soul-searching, the Paris of Jean-Paul Sartre and Simone de Beauvoir. Philosophy and art fused in an explosive combination. There was something else even more revolutionary than that though. A new summer fashion took Paris by storm in 1946 – they called it the 'Atome Bikini'. The one-piece bathing suit was replaced by something quite extraordinary and so small that it hardly covered the vital parts of the female body. It was named after the Bikini Atoll where the French were testing their atomic bomb. And it was like a nuclear explosion. Semi-naked women dressed in bikinis smiled out at us from the fashion pages of magazines and from posters in the department stores of Paris. Even the Pope got involved in the controversy, calling this new outfit sinful. It was some sort of reaction against wartime austerity. People loved it. They wanted to forget the cruelty of the war. They wanted to live life to the full. Alexander thought it was hilarious. He couldn't hide his satisfaction.

Initially he threw himself into his work with the enthusiasm of a little boy. His eyes were burning brightly again. During the short spells when Kolarov was in Paris, we frequently went to receptions at the Soviet embassy with him, where we met a lot of leftist intellectuals and politicians. Kolarov was very proud of Alexander. He himself was an educated man who spoke fluently all three major European languages – French, German and English. He had studied law in France and was a graduate of the University of Geneva. As a communist exile, he had lived in most European capitals. He was the second of the group of three Bulgarians at the Comintern in Moscow who Stalin trusted most, the first being Dimitrov. The third was Chervenkov but his name would be airbrushed from the history books after the death of Stalin. In the summer of 1946 all three were back in Bulgaria and had one thing in common – they had lived through and survived Stalin's purges unharmed.

Kolarov was very kind to us. He warned Alexander several times to be less outspoken in his conversations with foreigners – Stalin's spies were everywhere.

It was during that summer when I first heard of Angelo Cahan, arguably the richest Bulgarian at the time. He was trying to profit from Bulgaria's wartime debt and to retrieve his assets left behind in the country. Alexander said he wore an American army uniform. Angelo introduced him to someone called George Anderson who spoke perfect Bulgarian. Apparently, he grew up in Bulgaria before the war, where his father was the president of the

American college. Alexander confided that he thought Anderson was the station chief of American intelligence in Istanbul, and as such Bulgaria fell within his field operations. Unlike most of the Bulgarian delegation, Alexander moved freely in foreign circles without fear. People accepted him because he spoke French and English fluently. There was no one to practise his German with, but during that time Alexander read a lot of German philosophy. He was an expert on Hegel.

His work on the peace treaty was highly praised by everyone. All documents had to be drawn up in three languages – English, French and Russian. Alexander was perfectly suited for the job. Stalin had promised that Bulgaria would return to its pre-war borders without losing any territory. Molotov made sure that the other great powers fell into line. The Greeks didn't like it and were trying to extort huge reparations for the Bulgarian occupation and annexation of their land during the war. Tito's Yugoslavia demanded reparations, too, but we were assured that after the treaty had been signed these would be forgiven as a goodwill gesture to a fellow communist nation.

Every night, Alexander discussed the details of the treaty with me. He valued my opinion. That remained the case until a ghost from his past emerged. Her name was Lucienne Bovren, and I must admit that when I saw her walk into a room I felt myself old-fashioned and dowdy. She was older than me, but well preserved and very stylish. She turned up at the Hotel d'Orsay one day with some Americans. Alexander introduced her to me, but really, we needed no introduction. I instinctively knew who she was. I had felt her distant presence ever since Alexander's return from his studies in Paris twenty years ago.

The peace conference went on until the middle of October. By the end of it, momentous changes had swept through Bulgaria. There had been a referendum on the monarchy and the people voted for a republic. Dimitrov, who had returned to Bulgaria from Moscow as the country's appointed leader, became prime minister. A new constitution of the People's Republic was adopted. The Fatherland Front became the ruling bloc in parliament but we knew that this was only a disguise for the unfettered rule of the Communist Party.

Diplomats at the Bulgarian missions around the world, some of whom had been appointed by the previous monarchist regime before the end of the war, were recalled to Sofia. Most of them stared at the summons, and decided to seek asylum in the West. It was literally a matter of life or death: those of their colleagues who had for one reason or another gone back were caught in the meat grinder of the People's Court. The embassy in Paris, closed during the war, officially reopened, but there was no one to staff it. Alexander's skills were needed so Dimitrov asked him to stay on in Paris as a first secretary to our legation. I was in two minds. But we both loved living in Paris.

Just when I thought that staying in Paris would mean that his affair with Lucienne Bovren would be resurrected, he did something which surprised everybody. He brought Rosa Aronova from Sofia to work as his secretary at the embassy. Another blow to me, but I loved him so much that I had to find a way to come to terms with this new arrangement. Leaving him was unthinkable.

The peace treaty between Bulgaria and the Allied powers was signed on 10 February 1947. Stalin continued to play a game with the West, pretending that Bulgaria was not a client state of the USSR but rather an independent democratic country. He instructed Dimitrov not to come to the French capital for the signing of the peace treaty. Instead, Bulgaria was presented to the world as a country governed by a rainbow coalition, a happy plural democracy where governments came and went through democratic elections. The peace treaty was to be signed by the non-communist Kimon Georgiev, the agrarian Alexander Obbov, and the communist Traicho Kostoff. All three arrived by plane and were put up at the Hotel d'Orsay, where we were living.

Kostoff's career had suffered a nosedive since the return of Dimitrov. He was a home-grown resistance leader and resented the promotion of people who had spent the war in Moscow. Stalin had let it be known that he didn't trust him, and his removal from key positions had already started. But neither Alexander nor I ever imagined that he would be denounced as an enemy of the people and executed only two years later. When we met, he struck me as a bright man but he looked like a fish out of water in Paris. He didn't speak any foreign languages. He was instinctively distrustful of any Western diplomats. He was wary of the Russians, too, so he spent a lot of time with Alexander and me. He was a very entertaining companion. When talking with other people, he preferred to be seated because he had a pronounced hunchback due to an injury sustained in the course of interrogation at the Police Directorate in Sofia in 1942. He said his injury was the result of a fall from a fourth-floor window, but it was never clear whether he was pushed or whether he jumped because he couldn't stand the torture any longer. But when you looked into those black eyes, behind his round metal-framed spectacles, the spark more than made up for his twisted body.

The closeness we developed with Kostoff during those few days in Paris would later be used against Alexander.

18

1 November 1963

'In the summer of 1948, the director of the Central Bank of Bulgaria arrived in Paris to negotiate the purchase of debentures from Bulgaria's old national debt. I was asked to take part in the negotiations, not least because I spoke French. I had been living in Paris for the last two years and enjoyed great success forging valuable contacts with the French side. To my great surprise, we found that a prominent member of the delegation representing Bulgaria's creditors was none other than Angelo Cahan. The negotiations were very technical and I don't remember the details, but at the end Angelo asked me if I had been recalled to Bulgaria. I confirmed that both the ambassador and I had been told to return to Sofia for consultations. Angelo then confidentially whispered that we shouldn't go back because we would be arrested and indicted as spies. I was shocked by this revelation. It was hardly unusual for embassy staff to write unfavourable reports and even smear the reputation of their colleagues. This lay at the core of Stalin's doctrine of fear. But I was more interested in finding out *who* had given Angelo such confidential information, which could well have been true. He told me without hesitation that the information had come from the US ambassador in Sofia, Mr Hill.

'Dora didn't believe that anybody would bother to frame me for espionage. She was quite blunt. I wasn't important enough to merit such treatment. I thought that her analysis was quite sensible.

'On the following day, I arranged to meet Lucienne Bovren. She was pleased to see me. We had coffee in Montmartre. I asked her for her opinion about whether I should go back to Bulgaria. She was categorical. Defection to the West would mean that I would never see my country again. And she thought that I would miss it very much. How about the allegations of spying? I could get the death penalty for that even if it were not true. Lucienne smiled enigmatically and said, "It's not you who they are after. Stalin is very suspicious of Kostoff and is trying to get rid of him. Moscow thinks that Kostoff wants to deviate from the Stalinist model of communism. He stands accused of being in favour of the free market. Stalin also thinks that he is an ally of Tito. And the breakdown of relations between Tito and Stalin is happening as I speak." Good old Lucienne. Her brain was as sharp as a razor. Of course, it all made sense.

'In the summer of 1948, the ambassador and I returned to Sofia, only to be told by Kolarov, then foreign minister, that there had been some accusations by embassy staff alleging that both I and the ambassador were too close to some of the defectors from the previous monarchist regime living in France. There were also allegations that we were close to some shady businessmen. He didn't name any names but I knew he was referring to Angelo Cahan and to someone else who I only knew under the name of Silbert, a French-Bulgarian Jew who was also involved in the debt repurchasing. He said that comrade Dimitrov had vouched for us personally and that he himself trusted us completely. There would be no investigation into these allegations. He also made some flattering remarks about my work during the Peace Conference. Go back to Paris, he ordered. I couldn't wait to return… to Dora, to Rosa and to my dear Lucienne.

'By the end of 1948 some ominous news had reached us in Paris. The reports confirmed Lucienne's prediction. A visiting journalist from the Bulgarian news agency BTA told us of a secret meeting in Moscow between Stalin, Dimitrov, Chervenkov and Kostoff. At that meeting Kostoff was submitted to a humiliating dressing down by Stalin, who accused him of withholding sensitive trade information from the Soviet representatives in Bulgaria. Kostoff retorted that the USSR was buying tobacco from Bulgaria, one of the country's most valuable exports, at knock-down prices and then dumping it on the world markets for hard currency. Stalin apparently flew into a rage. He banged his pipe on the table and shouted about how ungrateful some people were for the Soviet sacrifice in the Great Patriotic War against the fascists. At the end of this outburst he stared at Kostoff in silence for a few seconds and called him a "crook". With that Kostoff's fate was sealed.

'Given Dimitrov's ill health, Stalin feared that Kostoff was readying himself to take over the leadership of the country. He had a strong grassroots support among the so-called "home-grown" communists, those who never made it to Moscow during the armed resistance and thus were not influenced by Stalin's direct indoctrination. Stalin's preferred choice for the leadership was Chervenkov, also a former Comintern operative. He was a younger man and totally devoted to Stalinism. He was also married to Dimitrov's sister.

'At the beginning of March 1949, while Dimitrov was receiving medical treatment in Moscow, Kolarov carried out Stalin's wishes. At a hastily convened secret meeting in Sofia, Kostoff was removed from the politburo. It took another three weeks for Kolarov to secure the support of the local party committees and only then was this decision communicated to the nation through the national press. What happened next bore the chilling hallmarks of Stalin's great purges of the 1930s.

'By the summer, Kostoff had been expelled from the Communist Party and had his parliamentary immunity revoked. And guess who had made the final speech denouncing Kostoff as the "enemy with a party card", demanding his removal from the Communist Party? One Todor Zhivkov, our current leader. There was something ironic in the fact that Kostoff, who had endured torture and interrogation at the hands of Nikola Geshev from the monarchist police during the war, found himself again in a prison cell. This time his interrogators were his party comrades. He was repeatedly tortured, beaten and deprived of food, water and sleep. Eventually, he signed a full confession.

'It was not easy to follow the developments from Paris, but when his confessions were published in the press they were just surreal. He admitted that he had attempted to organise the assassination of Georgi Dimitrov, stage a *coup d'état*, break away from the Soviet sphere of influence and achieve a union with Tito's Yugoslavia. The charges against him, which followed a few days later, were equally outlandish: treason, espionage in favour of the US, Great Britain and Yugoslavia, and economic sabotage. Don't you see the similarities, my dear major?' Alexander sighed. 'This is what you are going to charge me with at the end of this investigation.'

'It's too early to say,' Major Ohridski replied.

'Well, I haven't told you the best bit. In December 1949, I was recalled to Bulgaria again. I was asked to attend every single session of Kostoff's show trial at the Army Club in Sofia. Why did they choose this venue? Because it was easy to deny entry to party members who supported Kostoff. I was made to watch this broken man confess in a most humiliating way. He was a gibbering wreck. He didn't offer any resistance. He didn't make any last-minute stand against the system. Why? Because he believed in communism. I had the feeling that he was resigned to his fate and wanted the trial to be over as soon as possible so that he could finally die. This was yet another example of how the revolution devours its own children.

He was hanged a few hours after the verdict was pronounced. All politicians involved in his denunciation rose rapidly up the party hierarchy. The secret service operatives who had tortured him to obtain his confessions were rewarded with promotions and special commendations. I went back to Paris.'

19

Dora Ivanov

When Alexander came back to Paris from attending Kostoff's trial in Sofia he said we'd be next.

I didn't know what he meant. We hadn't done anything wrong. Dimitrov had died in the summer of 1949 during the purges against Kostoff and his supporters. Stalin's choice, Chervenkov, succeeded him as leader of the Communist Party and Kolarov became prime minister. We didn't know Chervenkov very well. He was a sort of propaganda man. His main preoccupation was to censor the arts, always on the look-out for subversive messages. He was instrumental in sending many writers, musicians and painters to the Gulags being set up to punish the old intelligentsia. He was very ambitious, so we were not surprised that he led the charge against Kostoff. But Kolarov, that nice avuncular man who spoke fluent French and told saucy jokes, we couldn't believe he had been so ruthless in pursuit of a fellow communist from the days of the armed struggle. Why did he send his comrade in arms to the gallows?

We marked New Year at the embassy in Paris with our stomachs tied in knots. In Bulgaria, following Kostoff's execution, a vicious campaign was unleashed against the 'enemy within the party'. Thousands of party members were being expelled and prosecuted. Chervenkov was using Stalinist methods to shore up his power base. New, younger people had been appointed to junior positions at the embassy and we suspected that they were

Chervenkov's eyes and ears. Alexander told me that he thought he had been followed on several occasions during his regular walks in Paris.

In May, both Alexander and his boss, the ambassador in Paris, were recalled again for consultations with the Foreign Ministry. This time the recall seemed more ominous because Alexander asked me to join him on the flight to Sofia. Alexander was once again the subject of an internal investigation.

The accusations against him this time were of a more serious nature. He was accused of making unauthorised contact with Leon Blum, the French socialist leader and briefly the president of the republic after the war. I knew that Lucienne had introduced Alexander to Blum and that the latter liked him very much. They must have met a couple of times. But back at home the leadership was increasingly suspicious of anybody who showed initiative in forging direct links with Western politicians without explicit instructions from Sofia. Bulgaria did not have any foreign intelligence service to speak of at the time, so a small department at the Foreign Ministry was receiving the coded reports from Paris. Alexander believed that his reports, which normally contained political analysis, lay unopened and unread.

When Alexander saw the foreign minister, Vladimir Poptomov, he seemed a bit disoriented. Poptomov, a decent man and a seasoned journalist, had a thick file in front of him during the meeting. He leafed through the documents in the file in silence and after a few minutes said, 'There are serious accusations against you. I don't believe them but looking at these documents, I think that some high-ranking members of our leadership believe that these allegations are true. There is a suggestion here that you should be expelled from the party and sacked from the Foreign Ministry. I think that your career in the diplomatic service overseas is over. Go back to Paris. In a few months, you will be recalled for good but I promise I'll give you an important political job in the ministry here in Sofia.'

Poptomov himself was sacked three weeks later.

Alexander didn't want to go back to Paris before securing a meeting with the new great leader, Chervenkov. That proved quite difficult. He tried all sorts of leads, including former colleagues from the Interior Ministry who had been elevated to high government jobs, but the wall around Chervenkov was impenetrable. Neither Alexander nor his boss, the recalled ambassador Vladigerov, were able to secure access to the leader. But one evening, quite by chance, ambassador Vladigerov bumped into Chervenkov at the opera. Chervenkov smiled and said casually, 'There's nothing to worry about. You and Alexander should go back to Paris.' The ambassador took the train to Paris the following day but Alexander was adamant that he was not leaving until he had a face-to-face meeting with Chervenkov. In his words, he had to clear everything up once and for all. Eventually, he secured an audience with the man.

Alexander didn't know Chervenkov very well but was told that Chervenkov was trying to copy Stalin in every respect. From personal experience, Alexander knew that Stalin appreciated directness. So he went straight to the point: 'I would like to know what crimes I have been accused of. If I have committed any crime, I am prepared to answer for it. But I am not prepared to have vile accusations against me swirling behind my back.'

Chervenkov shook his head. He was a handsome man with big hair which he wore in a quiff modelled on the Russian revolutionary poets. He had spent twenty years in exile in Moscow, and was married to Dimitrov's sister. The latter undoubtedly had played a role in his stratospheric political career. Chervenkov had something of the reputation of a lothario. No drunken dinner-table conversation among the newly minted high society would pass without someone airing the gossip that Chervenkov boasted the biggest dick in Bulgaria. It was always mentioned by men with a touch of envy, while women blushed at the very thought.

'There is nothing to worry about, comrade,' Chervenkov said. 'You are doing a fine job in Paris. Some of our operatives abroad can be a little bit, let's say, overzealous in their reports. A piece of advice from me, comrade, keep it in your pants. Don't think with your dick! People say that you have a lot of mistresses. That's a sure way for the enemy to get to you. It makes you vulnerable. You sleep with your secretary, Rosa, but our people suspect that she is a spy. We'll find out in due course. On another matter, if I weren't so busy, I would like to meet this Madame Bovren.'

Chervenkov winked conspiratorially and showed Alexander to the door. 'Go back to Paris!'

A month later Chervenkov's affair with the opera singer Neli Karova became public. We were introduced to her when she came to Paris for the peace treaty with Kolarov. She was the most beautiful woman in Bulgaria. This tumultuous affair, sprinkled with outbursts of jealousy on both sides, continued in and out of the public eye until her defection to the United States in 1960.

A day after his meeting with Chervenkov, Alexander was summoned to the Foreign Ministry. He was seen by the secretary of the party committee at the ministry, the de facto commissar who made sure everybody there toed the party line, and the head of Personnel. At that time, Personnel was run by State Security, who checked the background of every employee and vetted all staff. They didn't give out any details but just said that there were lots of reports against him from members of staff at the embassy, alleging that he was engaged in espionage, which, they emphasised, was a treasonable offence. It was made clear to him that these allegations had nothing to do with his extramarital affairs. Rosa Aronova, they said, was working as a spy for the newly created state of Israel and she was in big trouble. It was very likely that she would be expelled from the party. That did indeed come to pass much later, and she went off to live in Rome.

Alexander and I travelled back to Paris by the Orient Express through Belgrade in a first-class sleeper. During that journey, away from the prying eyes of the secret service, Alexander mentioned for the first time that we might be better off if we defected to France. 'We don't have children,' he said. 'There is nothing to tie us to Bulgaria.'

I wasn't sure how serious he was; you see, he was prone to such bombastic proposals only to discard them at the first sign of difficulty. I categorically refused to take part in any such thing. 'We can't just abandon our country at a moment when the revolution has succeeded and we are building a brighter future,' I said. I did believe in what I said. He did, too, but he was more preoccupied with his career. He was very ambitious and he was still bitter that he hadn't been given the role he deserved in the new administration.

20

2 NOVEMBER 1963

'THREE MONTHS AFTER MY MEETING WITH CHERVENKOV, I was ordered to return to Sofia permanently. We didn't have many possessions, so we loaded a couple of trunks on the train, said goodbye to Paris and after four glorious years in the French capital moved back to Bulgaria. I was given a job at the Foreign Ministry but I knew that I was out of favour. It was one of those situations when no one told you anything but you felt that the system was against you.

'I shared these thoughts with my old friend Nissim Mevorah. He had experienced the same trajectory in his career. After an illustrious stint at our embassy in Washington, where he became Bulgaria's first minister plenipotentiary to the United States after the war, and after masterminding Bulgaria's accession to the United Nations, he was also recalled and had been put out to grass as a professor at the law faculty of Sofia University. He said with sadness in his eyes that one needed a different set of skills to climb up the greasy pole once the revolution had succeeded. There was an intrinsic suspicion of everybody who had lived abroad and spoke foreign languages. We were outsiders and the new elite thought of us as potential spies. Although Nissim knew that this was all due to Stalin's attitude to intellectuals of all kinds, he didn't blame the great leader. Both of us remembered Stalin as a bright beacon of hope during the anti-fascist struggle. In our eyes, he could do no wrong.

'In May 1951, I was demonstratively sacked from the Foreign Ministry. There was even talk of my expulsion from the party. Those were dark days. Yugov had fallen from grace during the Kostoff affair but luckily he didn't follow him to the gallows. His life was spared and he faded into obscurity. I was going down rapidly into the political abyss but somebody intervened on my behalf. I suspected that it was Chervenkov who saved me from humiliation and, possibly, a long jail term. To this day, I can't figure out why. I must've made a good impression on him.

'I was given a job as an assistant professor at the law faculty. This transition from a high-flying diplomat, mixing with the great and the good at the Paris Peace Conference, to a lowly academic teaching Roman law at Sofia University wasn't easy. My relationship with Dora hit rock bottom. I started to see all my previous lovers regularly. I was horrible to Dora but she was so patient with me. She was a saint.

'Returning to Sofia was like going back to your grandparents' village after a long spell in the capital. The city had a dusty and provincial air. It struck me for the first time how Middle Eastern it looked. In Bulgarian, this look was called "oriental", like in the Orient Express, meaning Ottoman rather than Far Eastern. The Chervenkov government had started to clear the derelict buildings in the city centre destroyed or damaged in the bombing by British and American aircraft during the war. There were grandiose plans to rebuild it on the model of Stalinist Moscow.

'My dear major, do you remember what it looked like just after the war? All ruins and bomb craters, and low-rise shabby buildings. I prefer the way it looks now – the Communist Party House with the red star on its pitched roof modelled on the Kremlin, the Central Universal Store (TZUM), Grand Hotel 'Balkan' – all granite and limestone. These three buildings were like three sisters – similar but different. The centre of the city now looks modern, bright and clean. This is what we'll leave to the next generations. No one will ask if the population had enough to eat. The next generations will be looking at these buildings with admiration. This is an image of Sofia that our grandchildren can be proud of.'

Major Ohridski didn't respond. His new strategy was not to ask any questions but to let Alexander talk until he got tired.

'I didn't anticipate how rewarding my teaching career would be,' Alexander continued. 'The university was full of young men and women hungry for knowledge. Education was free. People of all sorts of backgrounds, mainly poor boys from peasant families, came to the capital to study. But there were young women, too.

'I was forty-four, with great legal experience, well-travelled, educated, wife-and-no-kids, and I hit a mid-life crisis. It manifested itself in reckless affairs with my female students, which got me into some trouble. My soul was in a dark place. I rented a small mansard apartment in an old Vienna Secession-style building at the back of the university and hardly went back to Dora. There were female students who willingly came to the apartment for sex; others I had to seduce. There were some who wanted money. Others wanted good marks in their exams. I have to say that, in addition to students, I went through all the university secretaries and typists like a plough through a field. I had a reputation.

'Then one day I was called by the party secretary and threatened with expulsion if I didn't stop. The meeting took place in a small room at the university. There were three of them. They sat silently while the commissar gave me a dressing down about the bad example I was setting to the students, about how patchy my lectures had been, and most importantly about how I hadn't attended a single meeting of the Communist Party cell at the university. All through the meeting I was thinking, who are these people? Who gave them the authority to lecture me? I didn't remember them taking part in the armed struggle against fascism. Had they been interrogated by the fascist police like I was? Did they know what it was like to countersign death warrants and have people executed in the name of the revolution? Did they know that I had sat with the leaders of the great powers in Paris mapping out the future of Bulgaria? They were intellectual midgets who had probably joined the Communist Party only to improve their careers.

'They gave me a final warning. I couldn't care less. There was, however, one thing I wanted to prove to them – that my lectures were brilliant and the students liked them. It occurred to me I should record them as proof of how competent and professional they were. I had also noticed that during the lectures I spontaneously came up with new ideas and phrases, which I forgot by the time I sat down to commit them to paper. This was how an interest in portable tape recorders began. I first acquired a small reel-to-reel Ampex recorder, which to the amusement of my students I placed on the lectern with an external microphone during my lectures. The fixed external microphone prevented me from pacing around during my lectures. I was told that one could buy an even smaller and lighter recorder, which could be hidden in a pocket. It was powered by small batteries and the microphone could be attached to your tie, disguised as a tiepin or even disguised as a wristwatch. That would've given me the opportunity to record my lectures while pacing casually in front of my students. Yes, I got one of those gadgets, but that happened much later.

'Rumour spread very quickly about the "American" recording equipment I was using during my lectures, and students from other faculties flocked to see me out of curiosity. That caused consternation with the management of the university but they couldn't do anything about it.

'A couple of years went by in this quasi-existence. I was already resigned to the idea that this was going to be my life until I reached pensionable age – a lecherous law professor with no major publications to his name, a broken marriage and a broken dream of becoming somebody of importance. I had a comfortable but unexciting life.

'At around this time, talk was circulating about Chervenkov's private life. Neli Karova, the beauty queen and opera singer, was his official mistress. Of course, nothing came out in the press, but our relatively small group of communist intellectuals, who knew each other from before the war, was well connected and well informed. With envy, we listened to the tales of those who had access to the corridors of power. We heard how Neli Karova had stormed into the prime ministerial office and thrown a tantrum, accusing him of an affair with a younger rival with a more promising singing career.

'With Stalin's blessing, Chervenkov had established himself as the undisputed leader. In Stalin's eyes he could do no wrong. After the deaths of Dimitrov and Kolarov, he had tightened his grip on power, on all aspects of life. Propaganda newsreels would show him in his trademark workman's flat cap and quilted labourer's overall, delivering fiery speeches at construction sites and factory floors. Workers and peasants thought that he was one of them. He was a propaganda man, through and through. He was tough on his opponents and ruthlessly crushed any dissent. But he knew the value of light entertainment for the masses. He encouraged and sponsored feel-good films, which the population loved. It was said that his reign was the golden era for socialist realism. He developed the careers of talented new actresses. Beautiful women had access to his office, according to rumours from his security detail. I was so envious to hear that a luscious beauty who had entertained the Nazis with her singing during the war had been giving him blowjobs in the office while his bodyguard blocked access to the room, even to people with urgent government business. I so much envied him.

'Thus life went on until something, though not unexpected still profoundly shocking, happened. Stalin died.'

Dora Ivanov

THE DEATH OF STALIN UNLEASHED UNFORESEEN CONSE-
quences for all of us. Alexander was truly saddened. Nissim
Mevorah cried when the announcement was made on 6 March
1953. Such was the deep-seated, unquestioning love some people
had for Stalin. For me, it was love for Stalin the symbol, not for
Stalin the man. Stalin symbolised the world revolution by the
proletariat. Stalin as an individual was a vain, insecure human
being whose main preoccupation was an unquenchable thirst for
power. That much I knew.

What we didn't know were the actual circumstances of his
death. The reasons given were ill health. He was becoming confused, even more paranoid than before and had lost his memory,
according to some voices. The rumour mill in the high circles of
the party in Bulgaria was already running at full speed. We heard
of plans for an internal putsch led by Beria, the much-feared
head of the NKVD and Stalin's executioner-in-chief. Alexander
couldn't contemplate a world in which Beria became the leader
of the communist world.

We knew that Beria was a capable man. Among other things,
he was in charge of the Soviet Union's nuclear programme. Due
to his efforts Moscow had caught up with America in the arms
race. We were elated when we heard that the Soviet Union had
successfully tested a nuclear bomb in 1949. It was four years after
the Americans but the communist world was finally standing up

to the imperialist powers with its own ultimate weapon. And Beria was instrumental in all that. But we also knew how bloodthirsty he was in carrying out Stalin's orders. We had heard about the black bread vans criss-crossing Moscow to snatch unsuspecting 'enemies of the people'. We had even heard about his sordid inclination for raping young women and throwing them out of his car like dirt. He didn't seem like a decent man.

Malenkov or Molotov, or even Khrushchev, would be more suitable to replace Stalin, but not Beria. Never. Alexander was often filled with impotent anger at the thought.

In our small world, the confusion around Stalin's death was obscured by a scandal at the university, with Alexander in the eye of the storm. A second-year student had told her friends in confidence that Alexander had offered her high marks in the exams in return for sexual favours. There was an investigation. He was reprimanded but kept his job. The row shattered him, and this was when he came back to me. He told me that he was determined to focus on his academic career and was writing a book about the origins of the state in ancient Sparta.

We lived in Alexander's house, which he had inherited from his father. The house wasn't very large but it was comfortable. Other communist apparatchiks had taken the luxury flats expropriated from former politicians and businessmen. But we were happy where we were and had created a very busy social life. Both of us liked visitors, so many people came to our evening meals; they turned into a gossip factory where the latest news from Moscow was dissected.

Apparently as early as 2 March 1953 Stalin had suffered a stroke. He had already left the Kremlin permanently and was living in his dacha in Volinskoe, a small village outside Moscow, once the preferred abode of many a prominent artist and writer. On the morning of 3 March he didn't come out of his rooms. His bodyguards were too scared to disturb him and only broke down the door after midday. The Great Dictator was lying on the floor in a pool of his own piss.

Beria, Molotov and Malenkov arrived a few hours later. Beria refused to call any doctors on the pretext that there was a Jewish conspiracy among the doctors treating Soviet VIPs. The so-called Doctors' Trial was still reverberating in Soviet society: some of the country's top physicians had been executed on trumped-up charges, accused of trying to eliminate the leadership by poisoning them. In a nutshell, the three conspirators let Stalin die before their own eyes. Just before the actual death, Stalin showed some signs of life and even tried to prop himself up on an elbow. At that moment, according to the eyewitness accounts of the bodyguards, Beria turned all sanctimonious and even kissed Stalin's hand. The official date of Stalin's death was registered as 5 March 1953. It was announced to the world on the following day, together with the announcement that Malenkov had become prime minister of the Soviet Union. So, the great leader was no more. We were stunned.

Many days of mourning followed, but the air was thick with foreboding. No one knew what was going to happen but we felt change was on the way. Political change for us meant more turmoil, more uncertainty. Alexander said that it couldn't get any worse for him. He was right. He was left alone to write his thesis on the organisation of the state in ancient Sparta. No one cared about stuff that happened two millennia ago. The university management thought this was a safe topic. How wrong they were.

By the middle of 1954, the winds of change which blew from Moscow had swept into Bulgaria. Khrushchev had re-established the post of Communist Party leader, which Stalin had neglected, this time under the title of first secretary. Beria got a taste of his own medicine. At a meeting of the full politburo he was accused of treason by Khrushchev. After a short interrogation at his old power base of the Lubyanka he was taken to the basement and shot in the back of the head by a senior army general.

Under the aegis of 'de-Stalinisation', and the removal of Stalin's personality cult, Khrushchev started dealing with his opponents. As de-Stalinisation was reaching Bulgaria, Alexander's book was published. It bore the innocuous title *The History of the State in Ancient Sparta*.

I didn't know what to expect. On the surface, it looked like a banal and boring history book destined for small circulation. But suddenly it elevated Alexander to the position of a big political thinker. He was feted as a historian able to foresee the changes now sweeping the Soviet Bloc. The book contained an oblique reference to the state of the economy not only in communist Bulgaria but throughout the communist world.

Pursuing military power, the leaders of Sparta, he wrote, had neglected the economy. The country was poor, agriculture unprofitable, there was no money to buy clothes and food. The Spartan currency didn't buy you anything because it was not convertible. Ships no longer stopped in Spartan ports, the government suppressed dissent through a vast network of secret agents.

My heart fluttered with fear when I read it. I thought that he would be arrested and thrown in jail or, even worse, confined to a psychiatric hospital. This was what they did with political opponents and dissidents now. But nothing of the sort happened. Alexander was lucky. The new leadership was looking for material to discredit Chervenkov's handling of the economy. Instead of the straight jacket and the psychiatric ward, Alexander was invited to give lectures to party officials. His name was mentioned in the top circles again. He relished the attention.

The denunciation of Stalin was decisive. Khrushchev's secret speech at a closed party meeting criticising Stalin was the beginning of a short-lived economic and political liberalisation. That filtered through to Bulgaria. Chervenkov lost his job at the top of the party in 1954 but remained prime minister.

I was not quite sure whether Alexander had written the book anticipating the change happening all around us, or he just wanted to vent his anger at the futility of the state-controlled economy. He began to develop a theory that the communist revolution, instead of benefiting the whole of society, had created a new elite intent on preserving its dominant position.

In debates with his colleagues and friends Alexander argued that the communist revolution had not succeeded in abolishing the class system, but that it had created a new ruling class. He knew full well that these views would be reported to the authorities. He would go on to say that in a state-controlled economy, this new elite was only interested in preserving the benefits it reaped and not interested in making working people better off. This type of society was doomed and the Soviet Bloc would never be able to compete with the wealthy and more productive Western economies.

Such words were heresy in 1955. But heresy was in the air. Alexander claimed that he had reached this conclusion independently of Milovan Djilas, the Yugoslav dissident. Djilas had argued the same point in his book, *The New Class*, smuggled out of Yugoslavia and published in the West. Djilas was jailed. Alexander was left alone.

In April 1956, only about six months after the publication of Alexander's work, at a meeting of the Central Committee, Chervenkov was denounced and removed as prime minister. He was accused of creating a personality cult similar to Stalin's. His economic policy was declared disastrous. Zhivkov, the former print worker, executed a perfect *coup d'état* against him and assumed the leadership. The Fox was clever. Chervenkov would gradually lose all his government and party jobs and would be sent into comfortable retirement, never to be seen or heard in public again. In order to secure the removal of Chervenkov and shore up his own position, Zhivkov brought Yugov out of the political wilderness and made him prime minister, a smart move to appease the old Stalinists. Things were changing, but with Yugov's appointment they were also staying the same.

Alexander was pleased to see his old boss back at the top. Yugov, for his part, never forgot his old supporters. By the autumn of 1956 Alexander landed a job as a counsellor with the Bulgarian mission at the United Nations in New York. He was reborn, rising like a phoenix from the ashes, he said.

22

4 November 1963

'YOU WANTED TO KNOW HOW I BEGAN MY WORK AS A SPY for the CIA,' Alexander exhaled heavily. 'This is how it happened. When I received my visa from the American embassy allowing me to travel to the UN in New York, I already had a plan.

'Dora and I travelled by train to Paris on 10 November 1956. Again, our luggage consisted of two suitcases. We were to buy everything in America. From Paris, we were to take a transatlantic flight to New York, my first such experience. On previous occasions, I had travelled to the United States only by boat, either from Le Havre or from Southampton. We stopped over in Paris for three nights. On the first day, I went to see Angelo Cahan. He had an apartment on Boulevard Haussmann, walking distance from the Arc de Triomphe. He had established himself permanently in Paris after our last meeting in 1950. How did I know where to find him? Lucienne Bovren gave me the address. I had been exchanging letters with Lucienne ever since my job at the embassy in Paris ended. Angelo looked pleased to see me. I didn't waste any time in letting him know why I wanted to speak to him.

'"My position in Bulgaria is becoming very insecure," I said after we sat down for a brandy and a cup of coffee. "It's only a matter of time before I am demoted completely. The new clique at the top does not trust me. They see me as an unreformed Stalinist. Khrushchev has unleashed a witch-hunt against people like me. As luck would have it, my old boss Anton Yugov is now prime minister and he helped me get this job in New York. But I know his days are numbered. As soon as Zhivkov feels secure, Yugov will be the first to go. If he goes, I go too. Then there will be no rising from the ashes for either of us."

'Angelo put his coffee cup down on the small table. His eyes followed the cup and remained focused on it. But I knew he was all ears.

'"Do you remember our meeting at Hotel de Crillon ten years ago – you, me and Cy Black?" I continued, "Is he still with the CIA?"

'Angelo's eyes popped up with surprise. He didn't expect such a direct question. His hand grabbed the brandy glass and he sipped from it slowly. "You made me an offer then," I said. "You asked if I was prepared to work for the CIA. Does this offer still stand?"

'Angelo placed the glass carefully on the marble coffee table. "Yes, of course," he raised his finger to stop me from interrupting him. "But do you plan to return to Bulgaria after your assignment in New York?"

'"I don't know," I said. "What I do know is that if I choose to stay in the West, I wouldn't want to end up a penniless émigré like some of those sad relics of the old diplomatic service who decided not to return to Bulgaria after the revolution."

'Angelo cocked his head. "What is so sad about them?" he asked. "Some of them work in our propaganda effort? It's a decent job. You can choose between the BBC, Radio Free Europe and the Voice of America."

'"Oh, no, do you know how embarrassing it is to listen to these broadcasters?" I asked him. "Have you got any idea how stupid they sound? They are telling people that after the uprising in Hungary, Bulgaria and Romania will be next to take on the communist dictatorships. But everybody in Bulgaria knows there will be no uprising. The majority of the people accept the new regime. Those who do not are either dead or in the labour camps.

The Bulgarians are mainly peasant stock. Although many don't like the forced collectivisation of the land, most of our compatriots are small-minded cowards, incapable of helping themselves. They always look to someone from the outside to come and rescue them. Well, there isn't anybody because the Americans aren't going to send in the troops. Those who believe that Britain and America would invade Bulgaria once an uprising started are imbeciles and deserve to spend the rest of their lives in the Gulags."

'"Wow!" Angelo exclaimed with a smile. "This is the best political analysis of the situation I have ever heard. Almost every defector who wants to work for the CIA has been giving us what we want to hear. And you are not even a defector, yet. By the looks of it, you still believe in communism."

'"I do believe in the idea of communism but what is happening in Eastern Europe now is not communism. The state-controlled economy is not able to provide for the population and people live in poverty. The elite that runs the country is only interested in self-preservation. Khrushchev is a peasant who bears a personal grudge against Stalin. You know Stalin used to mock him in front of everybody and even ordered him to dance the 'kazachok' after a few drinks."

'"I am sure the CIA would love to hear your ideas about Hungary, Romania and Bulgaria."

'He then asked me about our flight details and jotted them down in a small black notebook: "When you arrive at the airport in New York somebody will come to you with the words, 'I am a friend of Angelo's'. You can trust that man. He will tell you what the next steps will be."

'Angelo trusted me implicitly. He didn't ask whether I had been sent to him as a double agent. As a smart businessman, he understood what was driving me to such a decision. I wanted to live well. I needed money for all my mistresses. To hell with caution! If I was going to end up in a Gulag or, even worse, be condemned to working for life at a dreary university run by incompetent commissars, I wanted to taste everything that life in the West could offer first.

'The same evening Angelo took me to Hotel de Crillon for a lavish dinner. The hotel had become even more glamorous since I'd last been there. Angelo seemed even richer. Post-war austerity was long gone. You could smell the money in the air. The waiters at the opulently decorated restaurant knew him. Although he was in his late sixties age had been very kind to him. He looked elegant in his navy pin-striped suit and his shiny black eyes were burning with curiosity.

'The last few weeks had been very exciting on the international scene. The United States had humiliated France and Britain over the Suez Crisis by forcing them to withdraw from Egypt. The Americans had finally achieved their long-lasting goal of breaking British influence in the world, especially in the former colonies. This process didn't come without side effects. The ultimate beneficiary of the US foreign policy over the Suez Crisis was the pro-Soviet Egyptian leader, Gamal Abdel Nasser. Nasser's nationalisation of the Suez Canal prompted the invasion. This split in the Western alliance had emboldened Khrushchev to invade Hungary and put an end to the anti-communist revolt there. The Hungarian uprising was brutally suppressed by massive Soviet intervention and, on the same day we arrived in Paris, Russian troops ruthlessly obliterated the last pockets of resistance. The Hungarian revolution was officially over.

'"The Hungarian people were betrayed by the United States," concluded Angelo with a pensive look on his face. "This will have a more profound effect on the world at large. There's more to it than a revolt in a small Eastern European country crushed by the Soviets. It's a total betrayal of trust. We encouraged the Hungarian people to rise up against the Russians and then abandoned them.

From now on, no one in the world will believe that the United States will come to their rescue."

'After dinner at Hotel de Crillon, we went to a cabaret in Place Pigalle. I was nervous about my future as an American agent. But the smell of Paris, the pretty women around us, the champagne, and the cognac took my mind away. Capitalism was rotten, but it smelled sweet. I was determined to make the most of what the West had to offer.'

23

DORA IVANOV

ALEXANDER AND I ARRIVED AT GARE DE L'EST IN PARIS ON
10 November 1956 troubled by the events in Hungary. The train
journey through Yugoslavia was fraught with tension, the train
packed with soldiers. The local papers didn't give away much
detail about the situation north of the border, but we knew that
at least two-and-half-thousand Hungarians had been killed. What
was even more shocking for us was that several hundred Russian
soldiers had also died in the fighting. Khrushchev had just been to
see the Yugoslav leader, Tito, on the island of Brioni in the Adriatic.
Apparently, Tito was very keen for the Hungarian uprising to be
decisively crushed because of his own troubles with nationalists
in Croatia. He didn't want Hungary to set a bad example. It was
a sad turn of events with a regrettable loss of life, but Hungary
ultimately remained communist. Alexander said to me that such
a thing would never happen in Bulgaria but didn't explain why.

On arrival in Paris, he left me alone at the hotel and went out
immediately. I suspected that he had gone to see Lucienne Bovren.
When he came back in the early hours of the next morning, he
smelled of alcohol and cigarettes. He wasn't a smoker so I guessed
he had been to a nightclub. I was surprised and very disturbed
when he confided that he had been out with Angelo Cahan.
Alexander was prone to doing such reckless things. Meeting a
wealthy Bulgarian exile who had been declared an enemy of the
people by our government would land you in trouble anyway,

but enjoying his hospitality in dodgy nightclubs around Place Pigalle put him in real danger. He was leaving himself wide open to blackmail.

I knew that he was unhappy with his demotion over the previous six years. I knew that he was angry and envious at Zhivkov's rise to power, but he never did anything to help himself in his career. He had a burning hatred of Zhivkov and his cohort, and thought it was beneath him to socialise with them. He wanted to be invited to a senior position simply on the basis of his knowledge and intellect. But having a feud with Zhivkov wouldn't help. And how would a perceived friendship in Paris, with somebody known to be an American spy, enhance his career as a communist diplomat? Meeting Angelo was just asking for trouble. I thought these were the actions of a madman.

On the second day in Paris, we went out for a walk in the Latin Quarter. Alexander bought some philosophy books. He was obsessed with Hegel. He claimed that he was one of the few people in Bulgaria able to translate Hegel without losing anything of the original meaning or spirit. He then suggested that one day he might be running an international institute dedicated to the works of Hegel, an institute that he would create himself with funding from the US and the USSR. I said to him that he was daydreaming.

'Everything is inherently contradictory,' was Alexander's favourite line from Hegel's *Science of Logic*. There was a contradiction within Alexander himself. He could be very calm and composed, but suddenly he would do something totally irrational. As a doctor, I sometimes worried for his sanity.

During our stopover in Paris we visited our embassy in Avenue Rapp, just off the Quai d'Orsay, close to the French Foreign Ministry. The staff there were very friendly. Alexander talked to them about Paris, showing off his knowledge of the city. I detected a degree of puzzlement about Alexander's appointment to the United Nations.

My impression was that they thought of him as a loose cannon, with an instinctive affection for the Western way of life. I knew very well that he never wanted to pretend that everything in the West was bad. But we were in the midst of the Cold War. The Hungarian uprising had just been suppressed and Alexander would have done well to be more careful about showing his affection for all things Parisian.

24

8 NOVEMBER 1963

MAJOR OHRIDSKI THREW A NEWSPAPER DOWN ON THE DESK in front of Alexander.

'Here we are,' he said. 'You're front page news today.'

Alexander adjusted his glasses and scanned the front page of the main Communist Party newspaper *Workers' Action*. There was no picture of him but his name was written in bold black letters, followed by the words 'American Spy' and 'Traitor'. The previous day had been a public holiday, 7 November, the anniversary of the Russian Revolution of 1917. The authorities had finally decided to make his arrest public. He realised that the propaganda war had started, with him and the CIA as the main villains. The paper reported spontaneous demonstrations by outraged citizens against his betrayal. Students had gathered outside the American embassy to protest against what was described as American interference in our internal affairs. Alexander leant back on his chair.

'What happened when you arrived in New York on 15 November, 1956?' Major Ohridski asked.

'After sixteen hours in the air, we finally arrived at Idlewild Airport,' Alexander started slowly, as if to savour every second of a pleasant memory. 'The flight, I must admit, wasn't a very nice experience. It was too long, very frustrating and boring. I had a headache so I couldn't take advantage of the vast amounts of alcohol on offer. Other passengers got terribly drunk. I found my first transatlantic flight rather tedious.

'We both travelled on diplomatic passports so we were whisked through immigration. Once we cleared passport control, we had to wait for our suitcases. During that time, a tall, skinny man in a dark suit approached me discreetly and said, "I am a friend of Angelo's." I had never met this man before. He introduced himself as Bonar. He welcomed me to the United States in an officious manner and asked me to come with him. I nodded at Dora who was standing a few yards away and told her not to worry and that everything would be all right. He took me to a small interview room down a dark corridor a short distance from the baggage hall. There I saw none other than Cyril Black. Black shook my hand and greeted me in Bulgarian. "I'm really glad that we shall be working together," he said.

'He looked more mature, with receding blonde hair and wrinkles around his eyes, but still handsome in an American sort of way. Short back and sides, and clean shaven. He wore a tweed jacket with leather patches on the elbows, befitting his academic credentials as a visiting history professor at Princeton. Agent Bonar, although dressed more formally in a black suit and blue tie, behaved as if Black were his superior. He addressed him as Mr Anderson.

'After a few pleasantries, we talked briefly about our last meeting in Paris seven years ago. Black also wanted to know whether in my opinion it was all over for the Hungarian revolution. I said that the brutal suppression of the uprising had sent a clear signal to the rest of the Soviet Bloc that Khrushchev would not tolerate any disobedience. "It's going to take perhaps a generation and a change of leadership in Moscow for any such thing to be repeated." Cy Black looked disappointed.

'Bonar had been watching in silence. At the end, "Anderson" instructed me that in three days' time I was to go to the Croydon Hotel on the Upper East Side at 11 a.m. He told me to memorise the address. In future, any instructions would be verbal. I must not write them down. At the Croydon Hotel, somebody would make contact with me with the same coded phrase: "I am a friend of Angelo's." That person would instruct me how to send my first political report to the CIA. Anderson was very keen to hear my opinion on the situation in Bulgaria after the events in Hungary.

'The whole meeting probably lasted no longer than five minutes. When I returned to Dora, I said only that the Americans wanted to check my credentials. "You know how paranoid they are about communist diplomats," I added.

'Three days later, 18 November 1956, I got up early with a strange feeling in my chest. It was a grim autumnal day in Manhattan. We had an apartment in a brownstone on East 62nd Street and 2nd Ave, a few blocks from the Bulgarian consulate. I was excited about the prospect of working with the Americans but a niggling thought had wormed itself into my brain: was I a traitor? Was giving political analysis to the CIA an act of treason? The Bulgarian government was not interested in my political analysis. The Americans wanted it. What would happen if the CIA wanted me to do things that went beyond political research? Pass on secret information or even kill someone? Was I prepared to do that? However, I hadn't betrayed anything or anybody yet. I was not privy to any sensitive military or strategic information. If my relationship with the CIA stayed that way, there would be no reason to think of myself as a traitor.

'I said to Dora that I was going out for breakfast with some colleagues and took a taxi to East 86th Street. The taxi dropped me off at the Croydon Hotel, a gigantic stone skyscraper between Madison and 5th Avenue. I was expecting to be approached by a stranger but Cyril Black was already in the lobby with another man who introduced himself as Silence. I smiled and said, "Is that your real name or is it a reference to the type of work you do?" They both laughed in a rather exaggerated way. The waiter led us to a secluded table in the far corner of the restaurant away from the prying eyes of casual visitors and said quietly, "Your usual table, Mr Anderson."

'Over a breakfast of Eggs Benedict with fresh bagels and copious amounts of coffee, we discussed our work arrangements. I was not allowed to take any notes. Black repeated that I must memorise everything. Nothing should be written down. There were two main things I had to commit to memory. First, a phone number. If I wanted to make contact with the CIA urgently, I had to call that number, give my name and say, "I want to see a doctor urgently." Somebody would call me back as soon as possible, beginning their message, "Your doctor's appointment is…" giving the time and the address of the meeting.

'Secondly, I was handed a piece of paper with a bank account number. Silence said the CIA had opened a bank account in the name of George Duvall with Chase Manhattan Bank, New York. George Duvall was my new name, Cyril Black said. As far as the CIA was concerned they did not have an agent named Alexander Ivanov. I would be issued with an American passport in the name of George Duvall. The account had $3,000 in it. It was for me to spend as I saw fit. Now I had to deliver the goods, he said smiling. At the end of the meeting Agent Silence took the piece of paper with the account number and said that I could access the account just by giving the name George Duvall and presenting my American passport.

'In the taxi on my way back to the apartment, I began sketching in my head my first report to the CIA. It had to start with a memorable statement: "Bulgaria is the Soviet Union's most loyal satellite in Eastern Europe. It is only a matter of time before it becomes the sixteenth republic of the Soviet Union. Zhivkov, who has positioned himself as a temporary stop-gap supreme leader of the Communist Party, is expertly manipulating the de-Stalinisation instructions from Moscow and has begun the gradual removal of Chervenkov supporters from power. He has the backing of some senior generals, namely Bulgaranov, and he will eventually assume total control. In order to keep it in the long term, he will need help from Moscow. For the purpose of retaining power, he will be prepared to surrender sovereignty to the Soviet Union. There is no independent free-thinking intelligentsia in Bulgaria to stir up trouble. The working class is paid relatively well compared with office workers, and the peasants are cowardly. Therefore, there will be no repeat of the Hungarian events in Bulgaria."

'I followed that with detailed profiles of Zhivkov and Yugov, and other senior leaders. I mentioned my suspicions that Zhivkov had been an informant of the fascist police during the war. In conclusion, I said that although Zhivkov was considered to be an outsider with no grassroots support, his determination to establish himself as supreme leader was not to be underestimated.'

25

DORA IVANOV

WHEN WE ARRIVED THERE IN NOVEMBER 1956, THE SKY-scrapers of New York shook my belief in communism to the core. Although I had seen postcards of the city before, absorbing the reality with my own eyes was a different experience. It was impossible to describe with words the impression these incredible buildings had on me. Moscow had grandiose buildings and vast squares but this was different. This was thriving capitalism incarnate, a symbol of creativity and technological advance. I was truly shocked. Alexander seemed absent-minded, as if something else was bearing down on him. He hardly listened to what I had to say.

We were met at the airport by a man from the Bulgarian mission at the UN who drove us to an apartment in Upper East Side, close to the Bulgarian consulate. The apartment was furnished very comfortably and we made it our home for the next few years. The first thing Alexander said to me when we arrived at the apartment was that his job at the UN was very different from his previous diplomatic position at the Bulgarian embassy in Paris. The Americans were different, he said. They were fervent anti-communists and we should be aware that we might be followed. We had to take extra care about what we talked about in the house because the apartment was surely going to be bugged.

The first few months were very difficult. I was hoping to be able to work as a doctor. For many years, I had worked as a specialist in tuberculosis at the Medical Academy in Sofia. Not only did I do research in this field but I also saw patients on the infectious disease ward. Before the war, I spent some time at St Mary's Hospital in London. After the revolution, I was lucky enough to be sent on research exchanges to Moscow and Paris. I held a doctorate in prevention of bacterial infectious diseases. Surely there would be something useful for me to do in America. But as I didn't have an American work permit, my role was eventually confined to that of the wife of the counsellor. None of the wives of the other members of the mission were allowed to work. But both Alexander and I were very excited to be in New York.

1956 proved an eventful year for Bulgaria. Since Khrushchev's secret speech at the 20th Congress of the Communist Party of the Soviet Union, things moved very quickly for us. The speech was not made public for three weeks after it was delivered. Even then only small instalments started to appear bit by bit. When we found out that Khrushchev had talked about a 'regime of terror, fear and suspicion under Stalin's personality cult', we were dumbfounded. The full text appeared in Belgrade and was smuggled into Bulgaria. Thus, a large part of the population had access to it mostly by word of mouth. It described how Stalin personally had ordered the assassination of Kirov in 1934, one of the most charismatic Soviet leaders and a close aide of Stalin's. The revelation that 98 out of the 139 members of the Central Committee had been shot dead on Stalin's orders between 1937 and 1938, and that the executions of Kamenev and Zinoviev were carried out with the sole purpose of increasing Stalin's personal grip on the levers of power, sent cold shivers down our spines. What next, we thought.

There was a joke doing the rounds in Sofia, initially within senior party circles but later within the general population: 'On his way to the Palace of the Soviets near the Kremlin to deliver his secret speech, Khrushchev stopped at Stalin's mausoleum.

He prodded the dead body with his finger and shouted, "Stalin, Stalin." Only after he was certain that the dead body was not going to wake up, did he go into the hall to denounce his former boss.'

Merely a month after the speech was released, de-Stalinisation reached Bulgaria in a big way. Chervenkov's personality cult was denounced at a swiftly convened plenary session of the Central Committee in April, rather inconveniently for Zhivkov, who as party secretary in Sofia had just ordered thousands of placards with Chervenkov's portrait for the May Day parade. Chervenkov was removed and Zhivkov duly elected as party leader. Alexander's old boss, Yugov, was brought back as prime minister and we were dispatched to New York. It worked out very well for us, at least in the short term. In New York, Alexander found his feet very quickly.

This wasn't his first visit to the UN. Back in 1949, Nissim Mevorah and Alexander went there on orders from Dimitrov as observers to the second session of the General Assembly. Their task was to collect information about the workings of the so-called Balkan Commission investigating complaints by Greece of interference in its internal affairs by northern communist neighbours, namely Bulgaria, Yugoslavia and Albania. Stalin was very keen to see a communist government in Greece and had urged Bulgaria to support directly and indirectly the Greek Communist Party (KKE).

The machinery of the UN was familiar to Alexander, and he threw himself into work. By the end of the following year he was a well-known figure at the UN headquarters. He volunteered for various committees and being fluent in English, French and German soon gained popularity among diplomats, especially from the 'non-aligned movement' countries like Yugoslavia and former British colonies which had just gained independence. They thought of the United States as an imperialist power, but didn't like to be dominated by the Soviet Union either. One such diplomat, who was impressed by Alexander's ability, was the newly appointed permanent representative of Burma, U Thant.

We met him and his wife at a reception at the UN headquarters. I remember clearly their diminutive figures. They were involved in an animated conversation with Dag Hammarskjöld, the gigantic Secretary-General, who had to bend down in order to talk to them. We are not the shortest couple in the room, I thought with a smile. Both Alexander and I were quite short. There was instant rapport between U Thant and Alexander. They talked about the increasingly important role of newly independent countries like Burma in the anti-colonial movement, then gathering pace at the UN. Alexander also talked about how in ten years' time Yugoslavia as a non-aligned country would be more important than France. I did remember him saying something along those lines seven years before during the Paris Peace Conference. U Thant was impressed by Alexander's erudition. They were both interested in philosophy, literature and art. At the end of the conversation, we had an invitation to join them for dinner at the Burmese mission.

One other thing happened by the end of 1957. Alexander developed a close relationship with members of the Soviet mission, especially a young, educated man called Vitaly Ivanov. Vitaly was employed as a translator but his influence within the mission was disproportionately high compared to his lowly job title. Initially, he started asking Alexander to stand in as a simultaneous interpreter in various Soviet presentations to foreign diplomats. As a result, Alexander's reputation within our own mission and in the Foreign Ministry in Sofia went up exponentially. To be trusted by the Soviet comrades with delivering sensitive information in person to friendly and unfriendly diplomats was a very big thing.

The change of attitude towards him was palpable. On a couple of occasions, when the official in charge of the coded messaging service between our mission and the Foreign Ministry was on leave, Alexander was asked to deputise for him. This was one of the most sensitive jobs in any diplomatic mission. When he was the political counsellor at our embassy in Paris, Alexander had access to the codes of our legation, too. He was a swift decision maker. On several occasions, when our head of mission was absent for a month or two, Alexander was appointed chargé d'affaires. He loved this extra responsibility.

He also relished the business trips. He travelled regularly between New York, Geneva and Sofia. Every now and then he would visit Moscow. I learned not to ask about these visits. He would brush off the question with a smile and say that he was used as a diplomatic courier. It was good that he was trusted.

In addition, he liked to throw a party or even an official reception for senior figures at the UN. And if that was not enough, one day he came home and said that he had been appointed to lead the Bulgarian delegation for the forthcoming bilateral financial negotiations with the United States. The negotiations concerned the outstanding debt the Bulgarian state owed the United States from before the war. The total amount of the debt was calculated at $26 million, a huge sum of money, which was inflated by some uncorroborated claims by private US citizens. The US State Department whittled it down to $7 million – still a crippling sum for the Bulgarian economy. The irony was that the only person in the delegation who spoke English was Alexander. During the talks, the other members of the Bulgarian side found it difficult to understand what was going on. Alexander did all the talking. The rest were helpless onlookers. That opened a new can of worms – allegations started to circulate at the embassy that Alexander was using his unique position to carve out a hefty commission for himself in return for negotiating a bad deal for Bulgaria. These were of course baseless rumours, born of envy. The Bulgarian ambassador in Washington even petitioned the Foreign Ministry in Sofia to have Alexander replaced with somebody less 'arrogant' but was told that this couldn't be done.

Alexander loved every minute of it.

26

12 November 1963

'Comrade Ivanov, I have on file serious allegations against you by our former ambassador in Washington,' Major Ohridski started the daily interrogation session. 'He says that you manipulated the debt talks with the US in such a way that Bulgaria had to pay $1 million more than it should have.'

'What does he know?' Alexander answered swiftly. 'The members of the delegation didn't have a clue about what was going on. The only person who had any handle on the situation was a deputy finance minister sent from Sofia but he didn't speak any English. Our official interpreter didn't know how to translate the financial jargon so I had to step in and translate. That made it very frustrating for everyone.'

'But he says in his deposition that the Bulgarian side was prepared to pay $2.5 million. Eventually, we ended up paying $3.5 million. How do you explain that?'

'This is a bit desperate on your part, Major Ohridski. If you are implying that the CIA had asked me to swindle Bulgaria out of a million dollars, you are mistaken. The CIA were not interested in the negotiations. But I'll explain to you what exactly happened. Originally, the Americans declared that the outstanding debt we owed them from before the war came to $26 million. That included a substantial amount of money claimed by private citizens. Something along the lines of "I had a business deal with a Bulgarian company but the war put a stop to it and I lost, say,

$20,000." The Americans quite rightly decided to ignore this private debt, which should've been covered by business insurance policies anyway. The amount of government debt was calculated at $7 million. The Americans had already frozen or confiscated Bulgarian assets in US banks to the tune of $3.2 million. They were asking for the balance of $3.8 million. As a result of the negotiations, we only paid $3.5 million. Do you follow? I saved our government a lot of money. Does that seem like a fraudulent deal to you? Zhivkov was very keen to put the debt negotiations behind us and resume trade with the Americans. Without settling the outstanding debt, the US would not trade with Bulgaria, full stop. I did nothing wrong. If anything, I saved the Bulgarian state $300,000. Anyway, if we had struck an agreement with them back in 1949 just after the Paris Peace Conference, we would've got a much better deal. But at the time, we were instructed to cut off all financial negotiations with the US. God only knows why.'

'You say that the CIA was not interested in the negotiations. How come?' the major asked.

'No, not at the beginning while we were negotiating. But I managed to rekindle their interest.'

'How did you do that?'

'When we reached the final stages and the deal was in sight, I went back to Sofia to brief the politburo…'

'You briefed the members of the politburo?' exclaimed the major.

'Yes, I did. What's so surprising about that? I was the chairman of our delegation. But anyway, some of the politburo members were against paying anything to the Americans, others were keen to pay up and start trading. The CIA was very interested in this split. I gave them a report on the personalities from both sides of the argument.'

'Did they pay you any money for that?'

'No, I never asked for any money. I asked them to bring Tonka Karabasheva to New York. We've been lovers since 1944 and I missed her a lot.'

'You asked for what?' the major raised his voice to the point of exultation. His officious manner had been replaced by something akin to admiration for the accused.

'Yes, I wanted her to visit me in New York. She was on some scientific exchange in Paris at the time but the American embassy there wouldn't give her a visa. So, I asked the CIA to help. During one of the regular meetings at the UN headquarters, I asked Cyril Black to arrange a visa for Tonka Karabasheva. Cyril Black retorted abruptly that this would not be possible because there was no visa agreement between the US and communist Bulgaria. I then suggested that they should bring her to New York illegally. Cyril Black was shocked. He had never heard of such an outrageous proposal. But I threatened to sever my links with the CIA if they didn't bring Karabasheva to me.'

～

Karabasheva was flown to New York by special CIA plane to avoid immigration checks. Cyril Black personally accompanied Alexander's lover on the plane from Paris. They were not the only passengers on the special flight. There were others but Karabasheva did not know what kind of people they were. Alexander was only told about her arrival after the CIA had put her up at a hotel in New York. He rushed to meet her at the Beverly Hotel on Lexington Avenue and 50th Street. But she was not alone. Karabasheva was chaperoned by a young woman, who spoke broken Bulgarian and introduced herself as Mary. Mary's instructions were to make sure Karabasheva stayed out of trouble. The first meeting was a great disappointment to Alexander because the two lovers couldn't be alone. Alexander was given a key to the hotel room and they arranged to meet the following day.

But when Alexander arrived at the hotel and unlocked the room the next day it was empty. No sign of Karabasheva or Mary. In a panic, Alexander called the CIA emergency number and got through to Cyril Black who explained that while Karabasheva and Mary had been out on a walk in Central Park, somebody had rifled through Karabasheva's suitcase without even trying to conceal his tracks. The CIA thought that this was the work either of the Soviet or Bulgarian intelligence and the pair had been taken to a safe house until they investigated the break-in. The CIA was worried that if the Russians had discovered that Karabasheva was in New York, that would lead them to Alexander and he would be unmasked. Until the investigation into the break-in was complete, the two women would remain incommunicado at the safe house. Alexander thought they were being over-cautious, but there was nothing he could do about it. He had to wait. A few days later, Cyril Black called him to say that they were certain the break-in was the work of a petty criminal and it had nothing to do with any spy agencies.

When given the all-clear from the CIA, Alexander demanded that the pair be flown to Lake Placid in Upstate New York, a posh mountain resort and the site of the 1932 Winter Olympics. Under the pretext that he had to recover from some mild illness, the two spent ten days in Lake Placid on the CIA's dollar.

Alexander was emboldened by the CIA's acquiescence and demanded that, on her return to Paris, Karabasheva be given $10,000 by the CIA to help her with her living expenses while she was studying there. They pretended that the money had come from Alexander.

His demands in those early days working for the CIA didn't stop there. On another occasion, he asked the CIA to bring Rosa

Aronova to him. She was travelling on an Israeli passport so there was no problem with the visa. This time they spent a week at Warm Springs in Georgia, a spa resort famous for its beneficial hot mineral water. The place was made famous by its most illustrious visitor, Franklin D. Roosevelt, who went there for treatment after contracting polio in the 1920s.

~

'Did Dr Tonka Karabasheva know that it was the CIA who had flown her to America? Did she know who paid the $10,000 to help with her medical research in Paris?' asked the major quietly.

'Of course she did,' came the answer. 'She was a greedy bitch who exploited me right up to the last minute. You must have seen the last letter she wrote to me. It was in my wallet when you arrested me. She says in the letter that she was so angry that I had put down the phone on her. I just couldn't listen to her constant nagging any more. She had written to Lucienne Bovren to complain about me, as if Lucienne was my mother. She basically wanted me to leave Dora and start a new life with her. She called me a liar and a coward. But I could never leave Dora. Although Dora and I had been separated in the last year, I could never contemplate a divorce. And I was right. Dora is the only one who stands by me even now in these sorry circumstances. Tonka was a good mistress, a passionate lover I should say, but she was a big mistake. I bet she is now trembling with fear that she might be charged with espionage because she knew where all this money came from. And she constantly asked for more...'

'I don't think that Dr Karabasheva will be indicted for espionage, but her bank accounts will be frozen and the assets in them confiscated,' the major said impassively.

27

15 November 1963

THE INTERROGATION ON THAT DAY BEGAN WITH A GENERAL conversation about the amount of money Alexander thought he had received from the CIA. He corrected himself and said that the first account the CIA had opened for him with Chase Manhattan Bank in New York was in the name of Alexander Belov, not George Duvall. He had been given a false American passport in the name of Belov before they issued a second passport in the name of George Duvall. The CIA had in the course of the last seven years set up another three bank accounts for him in Switzerland, two with UBS in Geneva, and one with an Italian bank through which the CIA paid $300 a month to his lover, Rosa Aronova. Alexander said he always looked after his mistresses.

'I still don't understand what was so valuable in the information you passed to the CIA that they paid you in excess of $200,000?' the major said.

'Well, it was the political reports at the beginning. Of course, I also sent them profiles of Soviet and East European political leaders and top officials, nothing really secret. But one day towards the end of 1957, Cyril Black asked me to give him the codes of the Bulgarian embassy in Washington, codes used to encrypt the secret messages between the embassy and the ministry. He knew that at the time I was deputising for the embassy encoder who was on holiday in Bulgaria for four weeks. I said that this might put me in unnecessary danger. What's it with that code? There were hardly any secrets passing between the embassy and the ministry. It's not the Soviet embassy, you know, I said. But Cyril Black insisted. So, one day after 5 p.m. when everybody at the embassy in Washington had gone home, I opened the safe with the key I was entrusted with. The safe was almost empty. There were two files inside plus a thick brown envelope containing the codes. The envelope was sealed. Every time someone needed the code, the opening of the envelope had to be signed in a special book. After the code was used, the envelope was sealed again with the embassy seal. The code was changed every six months.

'I put the envelope in my pocket but curiosity got the better of me and I took the other two files out to look at their contents. One of them contained the medical records of the ambassador's wife – obviously she had been taking some sort of treatment in the US. The other was the embassy accounts. I quickly glanced inside and spotted that sums of money had been paid regularly into an American bank account. There was no name for the recipient. As I was about to put the file on the desk to look through it properly, the door opened without warning and I found myself face to face with the embassy's head of security, a peasant man in his late forties whose only qualification to work at the embassy was that he came from the same village as Zhivkov. "Oh, working late, comrade Ivanov?" he said in a friendly voice. Before I was able to answer, he spotted the opened safe. I felt the cogs in his brain starting to turn so I decided not to interrupt that process and continued to leaf through the file. "Just to remind you," he finally said, "after you finish, please leave the key to the safe in the security room. It hadn't been signed out." I answered that I would sign it in and out according to the procedure, and apologised for forgetting to sign the key out.

'That evening, I met Cyril Black and Agent Bonar at the cafe of the Mayflower Hotel in Connecticut Avenue, Downtown DC.

I gave them the envelope without saying anything. Cyril Black examined it with curiosity and after convincing himself that it was genuine, passed it over to Bonar. The latter looked at the seal and commented that it would be too obvious if they broke it. That would undoubtedly point the finger at me. I mentioned that the security man at the embassy had spotted me taking stuff out of the safe. That decided the issue. I was told to return the envelope unopened.

'These were the glories of international espionage,' Alexander said with bitter irony in his voice. 'The next thing they asked was to give them the layout of the safe room at the embassy. There and then, in the cafe of the Mayflower Hotel in Washington, I drew them a plan on the back of a napkin. The room was said to be isolated in such a way that it couldn't be bugged by the Americans. When people needed to have a confidential conversation, they would go into that room. When Zhivkov visited the embassy, this was where he briefed us on key party policies.'

'I still can't believe that the CIA paid all this money to you and to your mistresses just for these simple errands,' Major Ohridski said. 'Are you saving the best for last?'

'You are right. These were just the first steps; it was them testing my determination and my ability to deliver. The real stuff was yet to come. But at that stage I had no idea what it would be. You still haven't asked me why I was doing it. You haven't even asked me if I had told Cyril Black about the payments from the embassy to what looked like an American informant. But I'll tell you anyway. I did tell Cyril Black and Bonar about the payments to the informant. They were stunned, as if a bombshell had exploded. They looked at each other before saying anything. Then Agent Bonar asked me if I would be prepared to photograph the accounts file. They would give me a small camera the size of a matchbox. I refused. The explanation that I gave them shocked them even more. I said that the Bulgarians would never run an informant on American soil of their own accord. The Soviet KGB must be using the Bulgarian embassy as a front to run not only this agent but probably others. If you exposed any of these agents, the KGB would make sure that everybody who had access to the embassy safe was replaced immediately. "I can photograph the file," I said. "But you will have to promise that no one will be exposed or arrested while I am working in the US." They promised. I agreed to photograph the accounts file of the Bulgarian embassy in Washington.

'The micro-camera they handed over was a triumph of modern technology. It looked like a cigarette lighter and had all the attributes of a lighter except that it had no gas in it. If somebody took it in their hands it would look like a normal metal lighter which had run out of gas. I used one of the regular authorised entries to access the safe and photograph the accounts file. A few days later I returned the camera to Cyril Black during one of our rendezvous at the Mayflower Hotel. Despite Black's assurances, I knew that this act would probably send at least one, maybe more, of the informants to their death. They would be convicted of treason by an American court and end up in the electric chair or the gas chamber. But this thought didn't have any impact on my conscience. For me they were not real people. They were just abstract notions, characters in a novel. They were just like the rows of names on a piece of paper waiting for my signature to send them for execution in Bulgaria back in 1944. I was unnerved by my lack of emotion. I knew that I had lost my moral compass.

'Life, though, carried on. I enjoyed the high life in New York. I served the Russians. I served the Americans. I knew it could not carry on like that forever but the thrill of the chase, the adrenalin rush, gave me strength to continue.

'For the fortieth anniversary of the Russian Revolution, the Soviet Union launched Sputnik 2 in November 1957. It followed the successful launch of Sputnik 1 a month earlier. I was so proud of these achievements of Soviet technology that I couldn't hide it even in front of Cyril Black. Although I was spying for the Americans, deep down my allegiance was still with the Soviet Union. The televised failure of the US Vanguard TV3 rocket in December and the American dismay over its setback in the space race only deepened my satisfaction.

'Cyril Black and Agent Bonar never told me whether the information in the Bulgarian embassy accounts file had led to any arrests. But I felt that, in their eyes, I was worth the money they paid me. I was given the use of a safe house in Upper East Side New York. The address was 44 East End Avenue, a brown brick block of flats with metal fire escapes criss-crossing the facade between the balconies overlooking the street. I knew the apartment was bugged but I started using it as a love pad.'

The major finally interrupted Alexander's monologue: 'Did your wife, Dora, know anything about your work with Cyril Black or the safe house?'

'I don't think so. If she did, she never showed it.'

'Did she know where the extra money was coming from?'

'She thought that it all came from my salary paid by the Foreign Ministry. I was very well paid. Dora loved attending the lavish receptions at the UN. She wore lovely long ball gowns with black satin elbow-length opera gloves. I gave her a diamond necklace to go with her favourite outfit. I bought it in one of those shops reserved only for top officials in Moscow during one of my regular diplomatic trips at that time. She loved wearing it.'

28

DORA IVANOV

AT THE SPECTACULAR NEW YEAR'S EVE PARTY ON 31 December 1958, in the conference hall of the General Assembly, everybody was talking about the Cuban Revolution. The Secretary-General, Dag Hammarskjöld, cut a dashing figure among the foreign diplomats. He spoke to Alexander after the banquet. His tone was calm and measured but I detected anxiety in his voice. He asked Alexander if Castro was going to declare allegiance to the Soviet Union immediately after seizing power. Castro's guerrilla army had made advances towards Havana and it was only a matter of time before Fulgencio Batista was toppled, Hammarskjöld said. Alexander said that although Castro would look for support from the Soviet Union, he wouldn't be so stupid as to declare an outright alliance with Khrushchev. President Eisenhower had already said that America would not tolerate a communist nest in the Western hemisphere. 'First and foremost, Castro will look for recognition from the United States. What will happen next is another matter,' Alexander concluded, and smiled wryly.

When we woke up on New Year's Day, all the television channels were reporting that Batista had been overthrown and Castro had formed a government in Havana. My eyes filled with tears when pictures of Castro and Che Guevara appeared on the screen. They looked so young and handsome. The revolution had succeeded, and this time it was here on America's doorstep.

The US was quick to recognise the new government in Havana and four months later Castro made a two-week visit to the States. When he came to New York, he declared that his movement was not communist. He couldn't fool us.

All that time Alexander was very busy. I didn't know what exactly he was doing but he was having meetings every day. I learned that in his regular trips to Moscow and Sofia he made brief stopovers in Paris and Rome. I knew that he was carrying on with his sordid affairs but again I didn't have the resolve to leave him. Tonka Karabasheva was working in Paris on a research grant at the Institut Pasteur, and Rosa Aronova had established herself in Rome. I had no idea what Rosa did for a living.

After the launch of Sputnik 1 in 1957, Alexander got involved in the debate about the peaceful exploration of outer space. He said that the Russians had asked him to spearhead some ideas in UN sub-committees. There was more to this than met the eye. In the summer, the Soviet Union had successfully tested an intercontinental ballistic missile. Thus, the space race was intricately linked with the arms race. The Russians needed all available legal minds to work on their behalf to justify their striving for military superiority in space. Alexander was chosen to be one of them. Members of the Bulgarian mission at the UN in New York and some of the embassy staff in Washington didn't like that. It was déjà vu from our Paris days all over again. People thought he was getting too big for his boots. He, on the other hand, didn't do anything to quash these sentiments by appearing humble and contrite. On the contrary, he carried himself in an arrogant and self-important manner. I liked his intellectual arrogance but it was never a good idea to appear intellectually superior to your colleagues, especially in the diplomatic service. Inevitably, he created lots of enemies. Neither the ambassador nor our head of mission liked him. He repeatedly humiliated them in public by appearing more analytical and better informed.

I remember one such incident at the end of 1957, barely a year after our arrival in New York. We had just returned from Moscow where he attended the celebrations of the fortieth anniversary of the Russian Revolution as part of the Bulgarian delegation. Khrushchev had thrown a big party for communist leaders from all over the world. The buzzword during the celebrations was 'peaceful coexistence' with the West, although everybody was preoccupied with one single thought: would the Soviet Union be able to win a nuclear confrontation with America? Mao Zedong made three speeches, which made for very uncomfortable listening. One in particular, titled 'American Imperialism is a Paper Tiger', sounded brazen and insensitive. He said that China was capable of surviving a nuclear war. 'There are 600 million Chinese. Even if half of them were killed, there would still be 300 million left. I'm not afraid of anyone.' Referring to this speech and to the body language between Khrushchev and Mao at the conference, Alexander let slip a sacrilegious thought in an exchange with Dag Hammarskjöld in front of our head of mission.

It happened during an innocuous cocktail reception. He said that it was only a matter of time before Mao and Khrushchev had a quarrel because both of them wanted to be the undisputed leader of the communist world. And to add insult to injury, he continued by saying that he didn't believe China would overtake the UK in industrial production in fifteen years, as stated by Mao at the conference. Hammarskjöld was intrigued but didn't pursue the argument. I thought that Alexander would be recalled after such unguarded remarks. But he wasn't. I wondered if the Russians had told him to say that.

29

23 NOVEMBER 1963

'PRESIDENT KENNEDY SHOT DEAD IN DALLAS,' read the headline of the Communist Party newspaper, which Major Ohridski threw down on the table in front of Alexander.

'How can you explain that?' he asked sternly, looking Alexander in the eye. 'Kennedy is dead. This must be good for us. America is the enemy. But I don't understand America. Was he a good guy or a bad guy?'

'He was our enemy,' said Alexander pensively. 'Was he a good guy? I don't know. He pushed America deeper into the war in Vietnam. And don't worry about not understanding America. Very few people do. It is the greatest country on earth but it is also very confused. I am shocked by this assassination but not entirely surprised. America is a vibrant but violent country. We are just violent.'

'You are going to trial at the end of December,' said Major Ohridski, expertly changing the subject. 'I've been told to conclude your interrogation as soon as possible. But I feel I am nowhere near finding out what you actually did for the CIA. They can't have paid you all this money for nothing. Well, you say you gave them some judicious political profiles and reports.'

'Again, my dear major, you don't understand how America and the Americans work. They pay the money because they have got it. After Castro came to power in Cuba, the CIA budget ballooned. They got millions of dollars to topple Castro. They are awash with money. They have more money than we can possibly imagine. But I'll tell you why they paid me. Apparently, I have received $200,000. I never counted it nor did I sign any receipts. But it is a lot of money even for American standards.

'In November 1957, I attended the greatest ever gathering of communist parties in Moscow as part of the extended Bulgarian delegation. My job was mainly secretarial – making sure that all documents produced by the conference were properly translated into Bulgarian. After my return to New York, I wrote a report to the CIA addressed to its director, Allen Dulles. In it, I outlined the state of the communist movement in the world as I saw it at the time. I said that the Soviet technological advances, especially its spectacular progress in space exploration, was proving very attractive for fledgling anti-colonial and anti-American movements around the world. But the world communist movement was like a dragon with two heads – the USSR and China. The two leading communist powers had increasingly divergent ideologies. Mao Zedong derived strength from China's population, the largest in the world, while Khrushchev, having the nous of the uneducated but wily peasant, banked on Russia's future technological dominance. He believed that in twenty years the Soviet Union would overtake America as the biggest economic power. There would be no room for two communist superpowers at the top. Having witnessed Mao's behaviour at the Moscow Conference, I believed he was pushing for a more confrontational line with the West and especially with America, while Khrushchev's mantra was "peaceful coexistence". He wanted to buy time for the Soviet Union to develop strategic nuclear weapons. The situation was ripe for a split. This split would have a profound effect on the world. In pursuit of ideological domination, China and the Soviet Union might at some point become engaged in an armed confrontation or even a proper war. This would offer an opportunity for the US. If these future divisions were exploited cogently, the US might be able to drive a wedge between the two even earlier.

'The report was handwritten on more than twenty pages. I placed it in an envelope addressed to Allen Dulles and left it in a postbox at Grand Central Station. This box was in the name of Joseph Pachuta and was used for communication with Cyril Black. I didn't hear anything from the CIA for several months. When I met Cyril Black, Agent Bonar or some of the others like Jackson and Silence, they pretended they'd never seen the report. I was getting very impatient because I was convinced that I was right.

'In the spring of 1958, my relationship with Cyril Black had all but broken down. I said to him that he was using me as an ordinary informant, a low-grade spy to procure petty information. I felt that I could contribute a lot more to shape American foreign policy. I had a deep knowledge of international affairs and an analytical mind. But I was met with sneers and disbelief from Black, Bonar and the others. Almost a year went by with menial requests from Black about information into the workings of our UN mission, our embassy in Washington and the general political scene in Bulgaria. I thought I had been underused.

'After Castro came to power in Cuba, I sensed that American foreign policy became rather unsettled. Not only were they scared about a possible Russian foothold in the Western hemisphere but they also feared that such revolutions might spread across the globe. I had been thinking about getting in touch directly with the head of the CIA, Allen Dulles, but hadn't seen an opportune moment. Then, at the end of May 1959, such a moment presented itself. His brother, the American Secretary of State, John Foster Dulles, died.

'A few weeks later, I searched the telephone book of Washington for Allen Dulles's number. When I found it, I went to Grand Central and from a telephone box made a phone call to that number. A female voice answered. I said who I was and asked to speak to Allen Dulles. The woman replied very kindly that her husband was not there, and would I mind calling back later? I said that I actually wanted to send him a letter. If I sent it to the address stated in the telephone directory, would he receive it personally? Yes, his wife answered, he would. So, I wrote another letter. In it, I stated my sincere condolences for the death of his brother who was a great man and a skilful diplomat, although I had disagreed with some of his views.

'I mentioned that within the CIA I was known under the name of George Duvall. I didn't criticise Cyril Black and the others. On the contrary, I said that they were high-calibre people with whom I could do business. However, I felt that they were not using my potential fully. To prove that, I pointed out that during a speech in California not long ago Allen Dulles himself had used almost verbatim a piece of political analysis contained in one of my reports to the CIA. This concerned recent political changes in the Soviet Politburo, namely the removal of Malenkov, Kaganovich and Molotov and the role Marshal Zhukov had played in this reshuffle. My conclusion was that the Soviet Union was faced with the possibility of military dictatorship under Zhukov. In the Marxist political vocabulary, this was known as Bonapartism, derived from Napoleon Bonaparte's ideology of a centralised authoritarian state with a charismatic leader at the helm, anti-elitist rhetoric, support from the army and social conservatism. I said that I was pleased to hear him use my political evaluation of the facts, which only demonstrated that he valued my judgement. I drew his attention to my previous letter, in which I analysed the growing rift between the Soviet Union and China. I stated that this rift would develop into a spectacular row lasting for decades.

'I didn't think that anybody would be in touch with me and contemplated severing my links with the CIA. However, a couple of weeks later, a letter arrived at the PO Box in Grand Central asking me to attend a meeting at one of the safe houses in New York. The address of the safe house was 338 East 77th Street, again on the Upper East Side. When I arrived at the agreed hour, guess who was waiting for me there? None other than Allen Dulles himself. The director of the CIA had come to see me in person.

'"My people tell me that you are a madman," he said, smiling. "They say your idea about a forthcoming split between the Chinese and the Russians is pure fantasy. But I wanted to meet you in person anyway. I like people who don't doubt their own judgement. My old boss at the State Department used to say about himself, 'Often wrong, but never in doubt!' Ha, ha, ha."

'He wasn't mocking. He told me that as a young diplomat he served at the US embassy in Istanbul in 1921, during which time he visited Bulgaria. He was fascinated by Bulgaria's turbulent history. Later, as a chief of the Near East division of the State Department he developed an interest in the Balkans due to it being one of the most unstable spots in the world. I told him about my own experiences as a young man in Bulgaria in 1925 and the lawless killings of liberal intellectuals by fascist thugs. That pushed me to embrace communism, I said.

'"You are still a communist at heart, even now that you work for us," he said, looking at me without a trace of hatred through his round gold-rimmed spectacles. He leant back in the chair smoking his pipe, waiting patiently for an answer. I didn't reply.

'"Do you know that I once had a telephone call from someone calling himself Vladimir Lenin?" He smiled again without any irony. "We were so ignorant back in the spring of 1917 when I worked at the American embassy in Bern that I am embarrassed even at the thought of it. The February Revolution had already ended the rule of the Romanovs in Russia. The tsar, Nicholas II, was deposed. Lenin was an obscure figure among the numerous

Russian revolutionaries in exile. He wanted to meet a representative of the American embassy in Switzerland to brief us about his intentions to carry out another revolution in Russia. We made a few jokes about it and ignored him. With hindsight, we ignored him at our peril. I vowed never again to ignore anybody who has a firm certainty in his beliefs. That's why I am here and I am all ears. Tell me, why do you think that there will be a bust-up between Moscow and Peking?"

'I explained that there were already Maoist and Leninist wings in the communist movement around the world. Leninism is more pragmatic. It espouses the idea of "peaceful coexistence" and puts an emphasis on economic cooperation and trade with the West. Maoism is militant. It rejects cooperation with the West and is intent on instigating violent revolutions. This ideological debate only masks the real bone of contention – who will lead the communist world? The Albanian Communist Party is already drifting away from Moscow and floating in the Chinese orbit. So are some other communist parties in Africa and Asia.

'I recalled some of my observations from the recent Moscow Conference of the communist and workers' parties. The body language between Khrushchev and Mao was tense. Khrushchev thought that sending a satellite into space was a sign that Moscow was much more advanced than Peking and therefore was the natural leader of the left-wing parties in the world. Mao wasn't happy with the denunciation of Stalin and made that clear in his speeches.

'The Chinese are also growing impatient with Khrushchev's manoeuvres to gain control over China's military machine. They see the recent joint ventures with the Russians in building new ships and submarines as a way of Moscow asserting its dominance over Peking.

'At the end of the conversation I felt that Allen Dulles remained unconvinced by my arguments. He was very polite. He only said that he needed more facts. I replied that the facts spoke for themselves.

"'OK, I'll give you an example," I said. "What is the link between the Lebanese Crisis in July of last year and the Taiwan Strait Crisis a month later?" Dulles raised his eyebrows.

"'Khrushchev,' I said. "Do not underestimate this little man. He is cleverer than you give him credit for. After you sent American troops to Lebanon in July last year under the Eisenhower Doctrine to protect a regime threatened by international communism, the Russians saw how vulnerable they were. American firepower moved into the Mediterranean and there was nothing they could do about it. They resorted to diplomacy to save their reputation. Khrushchev proposed a summit with you in Paris to solve the Lebanon Crisis."

'Dulles blinked. He nodded and a faint smile of understanding appeared on his face: "And then Mao ordered the bombing of two little islands in the Taiwan Straits – Big and Little Quemoy; the Kinmen islands as they were known here? We thought Khrushchev was behind this act because he was arming the Chinese navy at the time. We cancelled the Paris Summit. Clever. But you are saying that it was Mao acting on his own who precipitated the Taiwan Straits Crisis so that we cancel the summit with the Russians? It could've been a coincidence? Do you have any proof?"

"'I don't have any proof," I said. "I only heard a fleeting remark by U Thant that this was Mao's doing, according to his source in Peking. Don't you see? Mao will not tolerate Soviet domination over the communist movements around the world. He wants to lead them. That's why he would do anything to upstage Khrushchev."

'Allen Dulles listened in silence. "You could be right," he finally said. "But we need hard proof, we need more examples." I shrugged. He complimented me on my impressive knowledge of world affairs. Then, out of the blue, he asked me about my idea to create an international Hegel institute with CIA funding and with me at its head: "Again, my people tell me this is a crazy idea. Why would we do that?"

'"Well, the institute would be in a position to gather up the brightest young minds of Eastern and Western Europe, which in turn would provide a fertile ground for recruiting intelligent spies." I went straight to the point. I noticed that his face twitched. He mumbled that it was an idea worth thinking about. "I know Black and Bonar think that I want to lead this project for personal enrichment," I said. "This couldn't be further from the truth. All the money that you've paid me so far has gone to other people – I haven't spent anything on myself."

'Allen Dulles got up without saying anything. We shook hands and he left. I thought that this was the end of my work for the CIA. Little did I know that in the next few years events would propel me to the centre of the American operations against the Soviet Union.'

30

DORA IVANOV

IT WAS ONE OF THOSE OCCASIONS PEOPLE OFTEN DESCRIBE in retrospect as 'once in a lifetime'. Khrushchev had decided to travel to New York for the 15th Session of the General Assembly by boat in September 1960. He assembled a grand party of faithful Eastern European leaders – János Kádár of Hungary, Gheorghe Gheorghiu-Dej of Romania, and our very own Todor Zhivkov. The party leaders of Ukraine and Byelorussia were aboard, too. To my greatest surprise, Alexander was also invited as part of the so-called 'technical team'. The technical team had nothing to do with engineering. It was a group of highly experienced lawyers and political advisers with international experience. I suspected that Yugov had used his influence to put Alexander on the ship as his eyes and ears. He knew that his days were numbered. As one of the last Stalinists in the Bulgarian government his demise was imminent. Zhivkov, with the help of Moscow, was establishing himself as the undisputed leader. Or it may be that the Russians wanted Alexander on board the *Baltika* because Vitaly had recommended him for his trustworthiness and his fluency in Russian, French, German and English.

The task of the technical team was to iron out the details of what Khrushchev was going to say in his speech to the General Assembly. The thrust of the speech was going to be that the structure of the United Nations was outdated: it failed to reflect the political reality of the world. Khrushchev had an idea that the charter of the UN should be altered so that instead of one Secretary-General, the organisation should have three of them – one from the socialist camp, one representing the capitalist West, and another one from the developing world. Khrushchev had in his sights the lovely Dag Hammarskjöld, who had been so nice to us at social gatherings in New York. He constantly attacked him for 'spreading colonial policies' within the UN.

Another outlandish idea promulgated by Khrushchev was that the headquarters of the UN should be moved from New York to Switzerland, Moscow or even Australia. The foreign minister, Andrei Gromyko, who was running the show during the voyage, didn't think much of these ideas. He always looked very gloomy and stern, but on the boat his face seemed carved from stone. I never once caught him smiling during the banquets and official dinners. Khrushchev considered him very weak and cautious. The only person who had some influence on Khrushchev was the Communist Party leader of Ukraine, Nikolai Podgorny. This was what Alexander told me after attending the private meetings of the leaders. Podgorny had a nice, smiley face and didn't like to engage in political discussions in public.

Khrushchev was a small hyperactive man who bounced around like a ball among the guests on the ship. His face was always suntanned – he liked the sun. He had two very prominent brown moles, one under his right eye, the other in the middle of his left cheek. On all official portraits, though, both moles were expertly airbrushed.

His eyes were very agile. They scanned the environment around him like a rabbit for potential dangers. He didn't like to have anybody standing behind him, not even his bodyguards; it made him uncomfortable. He liked to feel the empty space or a solid wall behind his back. I was told that this was a legacy from the days of Stalin's purges, when people were grabbed from behind in the street and thrown into black bread vans, never to be seen again. High-ranking officials were seized in their offices or while getting out of their official cars, inevitably approached from the back so that they didn't have time to react. He also knew what had been happening in the basement of the Lubyanka. People with impeccable credentials were very often taken into the underground cells by their own deputies, or other close colleagues who were then made to shoot them in the back of the head. Sometimes Stalin watched these executions through a one-way mirror on the wall. Khrushchev was the great survivor and he wanted to make the most of the good life as first secretary of the Communist Party of the Soviet Union. He liked a drink or two and to the horror of his aides he improvised his speeches, deviating from the script, often with detrimental consequences.

The voyage started on 10 September 1960. The previous day we attended the military parade in Sofia. It was the sixteenth anniversary of 9 September, Bulgaria's Revolution Day. Alexander and I had passes to watch the parade from the stands around Dimitrov's Mausoleum. Zhivkov and Yugov, dressed in almost identical grey coats, were up on the tribune waving at the people with their faces wreathed in big smiles. Alexander was very agitated; it bugged him being so low down in the hierarchy. He felt he deserved to be up on the tribune with the main leaders. I could never understand where this superiority complex came from. 'One day I'll do something that's going to make me more famous than those idiots up there,' he murmured in anger, and indicated the politburo by raising his eyes. I told him to shut up. If the plain clothes security men overheard him we would get into a lot of trouble.

In the afternoon after the parade, members of our delegation, including Zhivkov and his wife, boarded a special plane which took us to Kaliningrad on the Soviet Baltic coast. There in the harbour against the evening northern sky we saw the beautiful white silhouette of the *Baltika*, its contours illuminated by garlands of light bulbs like a Christmas tree. This ship was the most elegant thing I had ever seen.

We were shown to the second-class deck, where our accommodation was going to be for the next week and a half. The first-class cabins were occupied by the leaders. The bedlinen, the towels, the bath robes and everything else inside the cabin were like they were from a fairy tale. Our luggage arrived promptly, delivered by one of the cabin boys. We always travelled light so there was not a lot to unpack. I put Alexander's suits in the wardrobe to make sure they were not creased. He liked them beautifully pressed. There wasn't much else to do so I climbed on to the main deck. There was no one around apart from the duty sailors. The evening breeze had sharpened. It made me shiver in my sleeveless dress. I shut my eyes. Here we are, I thought, my husband and I are travelling to America on Khrushchev's ship. This was beyond the dreams of ordinary people. I had a wonderful career in medical science. Alexander and I had achieved so much in life and yet I didn't feel happy. There was something missing. What was it? The thought of analysing this had always terrified me.

'The northern breeze has an edge,' a man's voice boomed next to me. 'If you're not careful it could make you ill for the rest of the voyage.'

I opened my eyes. There he was in his navy uniform – grey moustache, square build, kind eyes.

'I can look after myself,' I said. 'I am a doctor.'

'I'm the chief engineer on the boat,' he said. 'I normally live below deck, in the engine room. Don't go up very much.' He was probably in his early sixties. I didn't know what to say, so I stretched my arm for a handshake and said, 'I'm Dora, my husband and I are here with the Bulgarian delegation.'

'Anatoly,' he said and shook my hand. 'We've commandeered this beauty from its regular service between Leningrad and London. I hope you enjoy the voyage and we pray for good weather on the way.'

The voyage lasted almost ten days. Every night at about 8 p.m. I went to the same spot on the upper deck where I had first seen Anatoly. Every night he was there waiting for me. We talked. He held my hand. Nothing else happened. He told me about his life, his wartime years in the navy, his daughter Tatyana, his wife who had died during the siege of Leningrad. It was one of the happiest times in my life.

Alexander worked during the day and most of the evenings. I joined the wives for various activities, from table tennis to lectures on the history of the arts. There were lavish dinners and cocktail parties but they meant nothing to me. I was willing away the hours until I would meet Anatoly on the upper deck at eight every evening. I was looking forward to seeing his kind eyes and lined face. After the voyage I was never to see him again.

We arrived in New York harbour on 19 September. The *Baltika* was moored in East River Pier 73 because of its proximity to the United Nations. We were told that we wouldn't be staying in hotels but on board the ship for the duration of Khrushchev's visit. This was to make sure that the Americans did not listen to the confidential discussions between members of the delegation. The KGB thought that no building in New York was sufficiently secure and the only way to avoid being bugged by the Americans was to stay on board.

This Russian paranoia was transposed on to the Bulgarian delegation. In a bizarre turn of events, Zhivkov decided to brief the Bulgarian diplomats working in New York on a bench in Central Park. I never found out what was so important in the message Zhivkov delivered to our diplomats to justify such absurd secrecy.

It wasn't too long, however, before we realised that such precautions were justified.

With a flourish, the Americans demonstrated to the world a few days later that they had a mole in the Russian camp by leaking Khrushchev's forthcoming speech to the General Assembly. Khrushchev was incandescent. He was a volatile little man and threatened to court-martial the KGB top brass. We all knew that Khrushchev would be calling for the removal of Dag Hammarskjöld. He had previously accused him of siding with the colonial imperialist powers in the unfolding crisis in the Congo. But to have the main points of the speech splashed on the front pages of the newspapers in black and white made him see red.

I didn't think much of the incident until one evening during a cocktail party on the *Baltika* when Zhivkov's wife and I were having an idle chat. She was a doctor, too, so we knew each other but weren't very close. Suddenly, like a bolt out of the blue, she mentioned there was a traitor in our delegation. According to the KGB, the details of Khrushchev's speech were passed on to the Americans by somebody from the Bulgarian group. Zhivkov was briefed by his security chief and the hunt for the mole was now underway. There was something menacing in the way this message was delivered to me. Its casual tone, the carefully chosen moment in the middle of a cocktail party for foreign diplomats: it was all calculated to extract maximum shock value. I gasped. Was this a part of the campaign to flush out the mole? And why me? Was Alexander under suspicion? I was certain that in such cases everybody would be under suspicion and thoroughly investigated.

When I told Alexander about this conversation, he just shrugged his shoulders; his usual way of saying, 'Nothing to do with me.'

29 November 1963

'I memorised the main points of Zhivkov's political briefing to our diplomats in Central Park. Then I went back to our house, despite instructions to stay on board the ship for the duration of Khrushchev's visit, and typed the information from memory on my private typewriter. Having finished that in less than an hour, I arranged to meet Agent Bonar at one of the safe houses, 338 East 77th Street. He responded very quickly and we met the same evening. After handing over the typed pages, I explained to him that in my opinion there was some very valuable information here. I was justifiably pleased with myself for having predicted the split between China and the Soviet Union. And Zhivkov's briefing to our diplomats confirmed it. He said that the Soviet Union would not push for UN recognition of mainland China led by Mao Zedong. The island of Taiwan, although belonging to the "capitalist world", would be tolerated by Moscow for the foreseeable future as the sole representative of China at the UN.

'But there was more. Yugoslavia, although outside Moscow's sphere of influence, would be considered a friendly country and its efforts to play a leading role in the non-aligned movement would not be sabotaged. This rapprochement with Tito would lead to a split between the Soviet Union and Albania. That would be confirmed later when the Albanians impounded two Soviet submarines in the Port of Durrës. Finally, he said that it was now official policy of both Moscow and Sofia to improve economic relations with the United States. That last element was very important. It paved the way for Bulgaria to become the first communist country to purchase a licence from Coca-Cola and build a bottling plant five years later.

'Bonar's jaw dropped. The CIA were getting a heads-up on a valuable shift in world affairs. But I also noted a significant shift in Bulgarian politics. Normally, the heads of state or government lead the delegations to the General Assembly. Initially, it was announced that Prime Minister Anton Yugov would represent Bulgaria at the 15th Session. But only a few days before the visit, the Central Committee overruled the Foreign Ministry and appointed Zhivkov, the first secretary of the Communist Party, to lead our delegation. Bonar wanted to know if this was done at Khrushchev's request. I said that I didn't know but I believed that Zhivkov had already been anointed by Moscow as the absolute ruler of Bulgaria. My forecast was that Yugov would remain as prime minister. At the time, I couldn't foresee that he would be demoted only two years later. After Yugov's demise I told the CIA that there would be no show trial against him and my prediction turned out to be correct.

'Agent Bonar was visibly impressed by what I told him. He also said that giving them, in accurate detail, the draft of Khrushchev's speech was one of my greatest achievements. He said that Allen Dulles had said some very complimentary things about my work during the last regular meeting with staff. At that point, had I asked the CIA for another $200,000, they would've paid it into my bank account. But I didn't. I never asked the CIA directly for money. They just paid it into my various bank accounts when they thought it necessary. I was wondering if I should tell Bonar about what Zhivkov's wife had told Dora, namely that the KGB suspected there was a traitor within the Bulgarian delegation on the *Baltika*. But I didn't. I knew what would've happened. Agent Bonar would freeze with his mouth half open. He would shout, "That changes everything." When in fact it changed nothing. There was no direct evidence against me. Everybody in Zhivkov's entourage, all nine of them, excluding the wives, would be suspected, except the leader himself. There was nothing specific in the detail of the information I had passed on to the Americans. Nothing would point directly at me. Dozens of people had access to the same information. This was not the time to panic. Zhivkov's security people, his closest henchmen, would be at pains to prove to Moscow that it wasn't one of our delegation.

'Oblivious to my thoughts, Agent Bonar seemed in a good mood. But I didn't feel too well. My health was deteriorating. My stomach ulcer was slowly killing me.

'A few days later, Bonar and Cyril Black met me in the lobby of the Sheraton Hotel on Lexington Avenue. They praised my work again. They said that Khrushchev, unpredictable as he was, would try to gather support from Third World delegates about his new approach to Congo and Cuba. I would make an invaluable contribution to world peace if I was to record his secret conversations on board the *Baltika*. They wanted to know his strategy. But that was not all. Moscow's current focus on Congo was very disturbing for the Americans. The Soviet Union was trying to turn Congo, just emerging from Belgian colonial rule, into a client state. The new charismatic leader, Patrice Lumumba, was leaning towards the Soviet Union. It would be detrimental to the free world, Bonar said, if the largest country in Africa became communist. As a trusted member of the Congo Committee of the UN, I was asked to record all the discussions of the committee and pass them on to the CIA. I said that I had a very good reputation among the Russian delegation at the UN. It was the Russians who had put me forward for membership of the committee in the first place.

'"How am I going to record these conversations?" I asked. "You can't expect me to take notes or remember every detail and nuance."

'"This is where this little gadget comes into play," said Cyril Black and he produced from his briefcase a small recorder the size of a cigarette lighter. "This is the smallest cassette recorder in the world. It has a recording time of three hours. The microphone can be wired from your pocket under your shirt and hidden in your cufflinks or tiepin. It's absolutely noiseless." I was so excited. I loved gadgets. "Can you make it look like a real cigarette lighter?" I asked.

'They looked at each other as if I had asked for a Christmas present. I told them that I had already used a similar Minifon to record my lectures in Bulgaria five years ago. It worked on the same principle but it was much bigger. And I didn't have to hide it, I said. They laughed.'

32

30 NOVEMBER 1963

'IN HIS SPEECH TO THE UNITED NATIONS GENERAL ASSEMBLY, Khrushchev demanded the resignation of Dag Hammarskjöld. I remember it well because I had worked on the documents for the speech while on the *Baltika*. It was 3 October 1960.

'This was Khrushchev's second visit to the US. He was more confident and his body language suggested that he had developed a strange love-hate relationship with America; he was in love with its way of life. And he relished the publicity. He had visited the year before, from 15 to 27 September 1959, meaning he was the first leader in the turbulent history of Russia and the Soviet Union to visit America, and he was very proud of it.

'His first trip was a media sensation. Even before his arrival, the press frenzy on both sides of the Atlantic was in full swing. Khrushchev's official aircraft, a brand new Tupolev 114, was the pride of Soviet engineering. It was capable of making the flight from Moscow to Andrews Air Force Base outside Washington without stopping to refuel. Before the flight, cracks were found in the plane's fuselage and Khrushchev was advised to take a different aircraft but he refused. To the horror of his entourage, he overruled the technical advice. He was determined to demonstrate to the world the achievements of Soviet engineering by making a non-stop flight from Moscow to Washington in a brand-new Soviet-built machine. The flight was completed without incident.

'The composition of his travelling party was also a sensation. For the first time, the Western public was able to see the family of a Soviet leader. He was accompanied by his wife Nina, son Sergei, daughters Julia and Rada, and even his son-in-law.

'In the Oval Office of the White House, Khrushchev presented Eisenhower with a replica of Lunik 2, a space probe which the Russians had successfully landed on the moon only the previous day. This present carried a great propaganda value. It was the first man-made object to touch the moon's surface and as such symbolised the great victory of the Soviet Union over America in the space race.

'But that was just the beginning of Khrushchev's entertaining roadshow. He met Eleanor Roosevelt and paid homage to the grave of President F. D. Roosevelt, a wartime ally of Stalin. In a meas-ured speech to the United Nations General Assembly he departed from his previous confrontational line, epitomised by the words, "We shall bury you!", and talked about the damaging effects of the Cold War. He declared that the competition between the two world orders should not be about who had more hydrogen bombs but who built more houses and produced more milk.

'He was visited at his hotel, the Waldorf Astoria in New York, by Nelson Rockefeller, governor of New York, and in the eyes of the Soviet public a symbol of rapacious Western capitalism. Before leaving the Big Apple, Khrushchev gave a speech in which he pointedly expressed his regret that he had no opportunity of meeting ordinary people: "The workers who are the backbone of the life in the city, the producers of its wealth." He was given the chance to be questioned by trade union leaders later in California. He complained that he didn't like the questions.

'In Los Angeles, he attended a star-studded luncheon at Twentieth Century Fox where he was introduced to Gary Cooper, Frank Sinatra, Elizabeth Taylor and Marilyn Monroe. During the lunch, he was told that his trip to Disneyland had been cancelled because of security concerns. The LA police chief declared that he couldn't guarantee the Soviet leader's safety in the theme park. Khrushchev was most displeased. During his speech at the lunch he made impromptu comments about how much he wanted to visit Disneyland. "Are you hiding rocket launch pads there?" he ironically asked his hosts. "Is there cholera or plague there? Or have gangsters taken it over and they want to destroy me?" Instead of Disneyland, he was taken on set to see the filming of *Can-Can*, a racy musical starring Frank Sinatra. Sinatra told Khrushchev, "This is a film about a lot of pretty girls – and fellows who like pretty girls." Khrushchev openly disapproved of the nudity in the film.

'Later in San Jose, on a tour of IBM, the Soviet leader seemed more impressed by the efficiency of the canteen for the employees than the computers. After IBM, Khrushchev rushed into a supermarket outside San Francisco, causing a media stampede. Customers and photographers swarmed the place trying to get a glimpse and take a picture of the Soviet leader while he was inspecting the deli counter and the frozen meals.

'In Des Moines, Iowa, Khrushchev saw a sign by residents reading, "We do not agree with you on many questions, but we welcome you." He famously called it a "sensible slogan". In a meatpacking factory in the city, he tasted his first American hot dog. His off-the-cuff remarks while chomping on the sausage were carried in a flash around the world by the news agencies: "We have beaten you to the moon, but you have beaten us in sausage making."

'Khrushchev was furious after his main speech was leaked and he instructed the KGB to conduct a thorough investigation. I knew what that meant. Everybody on the *Baltika* from the cleaners to the leaders would be under surveillance. This would continue until the mole was uncovered. An order was issued that even staff permanently based in New York who were part of the technical teams for the visit should live on board. This meant people like Dora and I. We were convinced that we were under surveillance on or off the ship. That caused a major inconvenience for my meetings with Bonar and Black.

'Khrushchev's performance at the UN deserved an Oscar. The new flashpoint in the world was Congo. He was angry at the UN Secretary-General, Dag Hammarskjöld, for his refusal to intervene in the conflict. A UN peacekeeping force had already been deployed in the newly independent Congo but it had orders not to influence the outcome of the conflict.

'His first outburst came during a speech by the British prime minister, Harold Macmillan. When Macmillan expressed full confidence in Dag Hammarskjöld and praised his energy, resourcefulness and integrity, Khrushchev pounded the table with both fists. Other members of the Soviet delegation joined in. It looked like a scene from a rowdy classroom.

'A week later, Khrushchev famously banged his shoe on the table when the Philippines' delegate accused the Soviet Union of imperialism in Eastern Europe. We both watched Khrushchev's performances at the UN with increasing exasperation. Even Dora commented that the Soviet leader was unhinged and that he would lead the world into a nuclear disaster.'

'Agent Bonar gave me the lighter-sized audio recorder with a microphone disguised as a tiepin. In one of the safe houses in Upper East Side, he trained me to use it. The most difficult part of it was to attach it in such a way as to be invisible. The thin silver wire from the back of the tiepin was supposed to go under my shirt and then through a tiny hole into my breast pocket where I had to place the recorder. You switched it on with a little slider on the side. He reminded me that Khrushchev was due to brief Third World delegates about Moscow's intentions in Cuba and the Congo. I didn't think much of such briefings because they were normally bland and followed a strict protocol. Khrushchev usually turned them into a rant against American imperialism so I never bothered to switch the recorder on. But on the day before he left New York, Khrushchev gave an extraordinary briefing on board the *Baltika* and I happened to be there. I counted only fifteen people present, including myself. Most of them were Soviet diplomats. From the Soviet Politburo, only Podgorny was there. The foreign minister, Gromyko, chaired the meeting in a conference room adjacent to the banquet hall of the ship. My friend Vitaly, the UN interpreter, and I were the only non-political staff. We were on stand-by as translators.

'The main guest was a young Latin American man who I didn't recognise. He was introduced as a personal representative of Fidel Castro. Vitaly was Gromyko's translator. I sat at the back. Khrushchev gave an impassioned speech about the heroic Cuban people who had risen against the imperialist tyranny. There was no substance in it but I turned the slider to switch on the recorder in my breast pocket. The little machine was so quiet that even I couldn't hear it. I wasn't sure if it was working or not.

'The young man spoke perfect English with an American accent. He conveyed Castro's gratitude for the moral and economic support the Soviet Union was giving to the new government in Cuba. But Fidel was worried that the Americans were planning an invasion of Cuba in order to remove the revolutionary government. Gromyko nodded and said Soviet intelligence had confirmed that President Eisenhower had allocated an additional $13 million to the CIA to overthrow Castro. Khrushchev became animated and began shouting: "What shall we do? What shall we do?"

'Gromyko assured the young man that Russian shipments of arms would continue with no interruption. Soviet officers would be deployed to train the new Cuban army to fend off any American aggression.

'Then suddenly Khrushchev flew into a rage. His face reddened, his eyes bulged, the vein on his forehead throbbed and he started to slur his words. All I understood was that we must do everything possible to protect the revolution and prevent an American invasion. I wondered if he had been drinking.

'Gromyko tried to calm the atmosphere by giving the Cuban more assurances. Then Khrushchev threw a bombshell: "We must deploy nuclear missiles on Cuban territory if we want to prevent an American invasion." The whole room went silent. Podgorny cocked his head towards Gromyko. My heart was pounding. I just hoped that the little machine was recording all this.

'Later that night I confidently walked down the gangway of the *Baltika* with the cigarette lighter still in my breast pocket. The two Soviet guards at the bottom of the steps saluted when I went past them. The UN building was looming large to my right. I only had to reach the end of the pier to be on safe ground. The entrance was guarded by American uniformed police. This was the longest walk in my life.

'I was worried that I might be followed as part of the general surveillance of everybody on the *Baltika* after Khrushchev's leaked speech. That's why I headed for our office at the UN building. I thought it was the least suspicious destination. There, I wrote a quick note to Bonar: "Need a doctor's appointment urgently", and posted it with the official mail.

'Two days later, Cyril Black intercepted me outside the General Assembly in the UN building. He was dressed in a grey suit. Gone was the tweed jacket with leather elbow patches. I almost didn't recognise him – he looked too formal. A large badge with his photo was dangling on his chest – press accreditation. It was clipped on a bright yellow ribbon hung around his neck. "I would like to give you the magazine with my interview," he said. "Meet at the Croydon Hotel at 7 p.m." I looked at my watch. I had two hours before the appointment.

'I had left the lighter on the coffee table in the sitting room of our apartment. I knew that in the aftermath of the leaked speech, the KGB would've searched the house as well as the houses of other diplomats staying on the *Baltika*. They would've searched my office, too. The only way to avoid detection was to keep it somewhere where everybody could see it. That way it would not arouse any suspicion. It worked. When I got back to the apartment there it was, still on the coffee table. I'd left it there the night after I mailed Bonar the note asking for a meeting. If anybody had inquired about why I went back to the apartment that night, I had a ready answer: "I had to pick up some research notes about the situation in the Congo."

'The Croydon was one of the most secure places for the CIA. Almost all staff there were on their payroll. The doorman recognised me and ushered me immediately to the usual table at the back of the cafe on the ground floor. There I saw Black and Bonar waiting with anticipation in their eyes. I placed the lighter on the table and casually said, "I'm sure you will like that." We talked about the weather for a couple of minutes before Bonar stretched his arm, grabbed the lighter in his hand, then stood up and excused himself. He had an urgent meeting, he said. Cy Black and I stayed on for a bit longer and then left – I through the front door, Cy through the back.

'I didn't hear from them until the *Baltika*, with the remaining members of the Soviet delegation, had sailed out of New York.

Khrushchev and his closest aides flew back to Moscow on the day after the meeting with Castro's man.

'Some days later, a letter arrived at the postbox at Grand Central congratulating me on the material I had supplied. That was the end of it. There was nothing in the papers about Khrushchev's outburst and the threat to deploy nuclear missiles on the island of Cuba. To me that suggested that the Americans were really worried.'

~

'As I expected, the Foreign Ministry gradually began replacing the staff at our mission in New York after Khrushchev's visit. Romanian and Hungarian diplomats were also recalled and replaced. I knew that the KGB were hoping to uncover the mole on the *Baltika* by a process of elimination. I told Black that I had to lie low for a while, but deep down I knew that my days in New York were numbered. As it happened, I survived there for almost another year.

'My dear major,' Alexander continued. 'Did the KGB tell you about what happened in the Lubyanka after they took me out of your hands and sent you to the airport on your own?'

The major pretended he hadn't heard the question.

'Oh, they haven't, have they?' Alexander's eyes sparkled with a rare expression of delight. 'They just tell you what to do. I'll let you in on a small secret.'

Alexander paused and looked at the window.

'They treated me very well. They didn't ask about the CIA, Cyril Black or Bonar. They weren't interested in my secret bank accounts or coded radio transmissions. Do you know what they really wanted to know?'

The major looked up in anticipation.

'They wanted to know what I knew about the death of Dag Hammarskjöld, the previous Secretary-General of the UN. I was a member of the Congo Commission at the UN. The Soviet delegation had put me forward for this position. The Congo crisis was very symptomatic of the Cold War. It demonstrated how ill-informed and short-sighted Western policy in post-colonial Africa was. In the summer of 1960, the newly elected prime minister of Congo, a young, charismatic man, Patrice Lumumba, came to New York to seek help from the United Nations and the US government to put down a rebellion against his government. He was received by Dag Hammarskjöld but President Eisenhower refused to meet him on the pretext that he was away on holiday. Lumumba wanted to steer Congo peacefully away from Belgian colonial rule. But he was considered too left wing and too close to Moscow. The CIA had already identified the man they wanted to rule Congo, one Colonel Mobutu.

'Lumumba was a dead man walking – unbeknown to him, the CIA had already received orders to assassinate him. His crime? Well, when he realised that neither Washington, nor the United Nations would help his government, he turned to Khrushchev. He was eventually deposed by Mobutu. But Mobutu found out, to his detriment, that holding a high-profile prisoner like Lumumba was a poisoned chalice because some of the troops supported him. So he sent him down to the breakaway state of Katanga, ruled by an unsavoury character, Moise Tshombe. It's not known how Lumumba and two of his friends died but rumours spread that they were lined up against a tree and shot one at a time by a firing squad. Protests around the world turned Lumumba posthumously into a heroic figure, and the new Congolese regime was feeling the pressure. Lumumba's corpse was dug up, chopped up and dissolved in sulphuric acid to obliterate any trace of his existence. Khrushchev created a university in Moscow bearing Lumumba's name to educate and indoctrinate communist sympathisers from the Third World. Many ANC activists received their training there.

'Khrushchev accused Dag Hammarskjöld of complicity in Lumumba's death. In September 1961, Dag went to negotiate a ceasefire between Tshombe's forces and UN peacekeepers he had sent to Katanga a year earlier. His plane crashed in Northern Rhodesia. All fifteen on board died. The circumstances of the crash remained unclear.

'But I had my suspicions that Hammarskjöld was murdered by Khrushchev,' Alexander said slowly. 'The KGB wanted to find out what I knew about the UN investigation into Hammarskjöld's death. I had no insider information and the KGB believed me. But it was common knowledge that Khrushchev wanted him out of the way.

'After the death of Dag Hammarskjöld, Agent Bonar, who had taken over as my handler from Cyril Black, and I had a serious conversation about my future. I said that I would be a very suitable candidate to become the Secretary-General of the UN. Bonar looked a bit distressed by this proposal but I said that if the CIA helped me put forward my application, I would stand a good chance. Bonar replied that my reputation within UN circles was excellent. Members of the secretariat and many delegates had spoken very highly of my abilities. However, American public opinion was not ready for a representative of a communist country to become Secretary-General of the United Nations. The Western countries would oppose my nomination. Still, I stood a very good chance for one of the undersecretary jobs. There were seven of them. Bonar said I would make an excellent undersecretary. The nomination, though, should come from the Bulgarian government.

'When I finally managed to speak to my direct boss, the Bulgarian foreign minister Karlo Lukanov, U Thant had already been appointed Secretary-General. U Thant was a great man. He was a quiet character, a devout Buddhist who believed in peace and peaceful negotiations. In private conversations he was funny and mischievous. We were lucky enough to be invited by his wife a few times to dinner at his private residence. Dora was very disappointed that we couldn't reciprocate and invite them back: it wasn't appropriate for a low-ranking Bulgarian diplomat to entertain the Secretary-General, no matter how well we got on.

'When I said that I was looking for a permanent job at the UN, his eyes twinkled behind his dark-rimmed glasses and a faint smile appeared on his face. He suggested that if the Bulgarian side put me forward, he would give me a very senior job with the secretariat. Lukanov listened to me and said, "Well, I shall have to report that to the politburo." Nothing came out of it. I don't think he ever mentioned it to anybody.'

33

During one of his regular trips from New York to Sofia, Alexander stopped over in Rome to see his lover, Rosa Aronova. It was 17 July 1961. He stayed in an inexpensive hotel in a slightly less fashionable part of central Rome, just off Piazza Barberini. The palatial suburban villa of the Bulgarian embassy was a fair distance away to the north, beyond the park of Villa Borghese, so there was less likelihood that he would bump into a member of staff. He wasn't planning to visit the embassy anyway. He was looking forward to seeing Rosa, who, after leaving the embassy in Paris, had acquired an Israeli passport. She had found a clerical job in Rome.

On the morning after his arrival, he was reading in bed when the telephone rang. It was the receptionist. There was a gentleman downstairs who wished to speak with him. Alexander was annoyed because he was not expecting any visitors. He thought that the Bulgarian embassy had tracked him down and was checking on him. He asked for the gentleman's name. After a few seconds, the reply came back: Nikola Geshev.

This was the name he least expected to hear. Alexander shivered. After all these years, this name provoked the same reaction. That man had done despicable things. There was a lot of speculation about Geshev's fate after the communist coup of September 1944. Some said he had escaped to Turkey with the whole police archive. Others were convinced that he was killed much later when he tried to cross the border disguised as a shepherd. It must have been unnerving for quite a few people in Bulgaria not knowing what exactly had happened to Geshev. The possibility that Geshev and his archive might resurface one day had preoccupied Alexander's mind, too. Although he hadn't betrayed anybody, what if the old puppet master had concocted something in the archive to implicate him? Was he there to blackmail him?

There was an elderly gentleman in the reception room sitting with his back to the stairs. When he turned, Alexander gasped. It really was Nikola Geshev. Dressed in a pin-striped suit and no tie, the man smiled at him. He looked much older, his hair had thinned to the point of going completely bald, and he had put on weight. Although it was almost twenty years since their last encounter, the man was unmistakably the Bulgarian super-policeman of the old fascist regime.

'I didn't want to surprise you but Cyril Black said that you were passing through Rome and I wanted to take the opportunity to see you again,' Geshev said in Bulgarian.

Alexander looked at the receptionist, who avoided his eyes and pretended to be busy writing something in a big notebook. It was common practice that all hotel staff in Rome were police informants.

Geshev read his mind: 'Yes, shall we go out for coffee in the square? I know a good place just a couple of minutes away overlooking the fountain.'

Alexander acknowledged this by an almost invisible nod of his head.

They sat down at a small table on the pavement in Piazza Barberini. Geshev ordered two small coffees and some Italian pastries. Alexander was impressed by Geshev's smooth Italian accent but then remembered that before he joined the police in the 1920s Geshev had studied law in Rome for two years.

'I have discussed your work with Cyril Black and have been impressed by what he told me,' Geshev continued. 'And I understand from him that you and I have similar views on certain things.' Both of them sipped from their coffees. Alexander maintained his silence. Geshev's hand, mottled with liver spots, put the empty coffee cup down.

'For example, I think that Radio Free Europe broadcasts elementary propaganda to Bulgaria, which most Bulgarians find stupid and out of touch with reality. Even the accents of the broadcasters sound foreign and untrustworthy. The BBC is slightly better but still its broadcasts don't chime with ordinary Bulgarians. They speak to people who have always opposed the communist regime. We don't need to convert those people. We need to speak to the broader public. I know that you think the same.'

Alexander cleared his throat but didn't say anything.

'What I mean is that you and I understand what's going on in Bulgaria, while people like Cyril Black, and the rest, don't. Their job is to undermine the regime but the CIA is pursuing the wrong tactic. They won't be successful unless they convert people like you, people in power. I've said it before, I'll say it again. The communists would govern Bulgaria for fifty years. We shall be long gone by then. But we can prepare the ground for their collapse now.'

'If propaganda is what you want to talk about, I don't have time for it. I have an appointment in about an hour,' Alexander said, breaking his silence.

'No, not at all. I'll leave the propaganda to other people. I am here about something completely different. The CIA and Cyril Black in particular have become unsure about your loyalties. To put it bluntly, they think that you are a double agent,' Geshev said. He paused with his eyes fixed on Alexander's. Alexander didn't react.

'And what do you think?' Alexander finally said, with a degree of irony to his voice. There was no smile on his face.

'Well, I have been asked to investigate. I haven't come up with a conclusion yet but I have built a psychological profile of you.

Correct me if I am wrong but I think that you *want* to be a double agent, but neither the Soviets nor the Bulgarians have yet asked you to spy for them. You occasionally send your reports to the Foreign Ministry with your views on the international situation but you know that no one reads them, and no one takes any notice of them. The only people who pay any attention to what you have to say are the agents at the CIA. It took them a long time to take you seriously. But now they do. Am I right?'

The clinical brutality of Geshev's assessment left Alexander breathless.

'My ulcer is killing me,' he said. 'I didn't take my medication this morning. I've got high blood pressure too.'

That bought him some time. It was unnerving to have a conversation with a man he thought had been dead for years. Cyril Black never mentioned that Geshev was alive, let alone that he was working for the CIA. But here he was, sitting in front of him. His calm, monotonous voice, his neat pin-striped suit, his unassuming avuncular look, the hand with the liver spots holding the empty cup of coffee – it all seemed to Alexander like a scene from a horror film. There was something menacing in his calm demeanour, not like the chumminess of those agents from the CIA.

'You know, when I left Bulgaria on 7 September 1944 I took all of my archive with me and handed it over to the Americans in Turkey. That was my insurance policy and my pension. I have enough incriminating material to bring the current leadership in Bulgaria down. But what would be the point? Other people will take their place and communism will remain. But with your help we can use it selectively as leverage against some individuals in power. The CIA are hopeless. They haven't got anyone on the inside. You are the only one.'

Alexander's eyes brightened up.

'I think you should become a double agent,' Geshev said matter-of-factly.

That was unexpected. Alexander blinked helplessly. 'What do you mean?' he asked.

'I mean that you should offer your services to the Bulgarian foreign intelligence. That way you will have access to more senior people in power. You might even become a member of the Central Committee. Cyril Black thinks that you can do it.'

So this was the game on offer. My kind of game, Alexander thought; a game of influence. But it carried its own risks – one wrong step and he'd lose everything. He could end up dead on the first attempt to blackmail someone in power. Alexander looked at the baroque fountain in the square. The muscular torso of the Greek god, Triton, son of Poseidon, was bathing in the foaming water. The messenger of the sea was kneeling on the joined tailfins of four dolphins as if waiting to be beheaded. Was this an auspicious sign or a warning?

To an outsider, they looked like two middle-aged men enjoying a cup of coffee in the morning sun.

'What do you think?' Geshev prompted.

'I can consider it. Do you remember what you told me back in 1943? Those who survive will reap all the benefits. Zhivkov followed that advice. But what you are asking me now is a matter of life or death. I may not survive to see the results of this game.'

'Ah, Zhivkov. He was an exceptionally slippery character. You should've realised by now that revolutions are never won on the barricades. They are won in the aftermath. Zhivkov tried to get rid of his potential rivals before the war was over. Now Yugov stands between him and absolute power. We can stop him.'

'Did he really betray anyone to you?' Alexander asked sheepishly.

'This will be revealed in due course. Are you up for it?'

'Yes, but what is the proof? A piece of paper with his signature would mean nothing twenty years after the events. You can't testify because you are the enemy, a witness discredited by history...'

'This is where you're wrong. There are people in Bulgaria who can testify to that. I can supply the names. You need to make a credible approach to them. It is going to be a delicate game.'

34

May 1962

From the Interior Ministry Archive

THE SECOND SECRETARY OF THE AMERICAN EMBASSY IN SOFIA, George Blackwell, left his office at 11 a.m. The embassy building in the centre of the city was under constant observation. The Bulgarian secret service would routinely follow all members of staff. Blackwell must have been aware that he was followed. He aimlessly walked the streets for about fifteen minutes, occasionally stopping at shop windows, hoping that he would notice in the reflection if anybody was tailing him. When he was convinced that it was all clear, he walked to the nearby central post office and dropped a letter in one of the postboxes at the front of the building.

A few minutes after he left the scene, a member of the Bulgarian secret service approached the postbox with one of the duty post-masters. They emptied the box. The agent took away all fourteen letters from the box for examination. By the evening all of them had been opened and read. There was nothing suspicious in any of them. They had also been checked for invisible ink. The test produced nothing. But one envelope drew the attention of the agents. The paper was thicker and looked expensive. It had no sender address on the back. Its contents were trivial and it was simply signed 'Peter'. The envelope was addressed to Alexander Ivanov. The name didn't mean anything to them. All letters had been duly resealed and on the following day they were sent back in the post.

By the evening, another agent had been asked to take a look at the names and addresses of the fourteen letters. He was a man in his fifties, who had spent all his career in the secret service from the early days of the regime. The agent remembered that in the period 1951–53, one Alexander Ivanov, assistant professor in the law faculty and a former diplomat in Paris, had been investigated for espionage, allegedly working for the French Intelligence Service. He remembered that nothing had come of the investigation. It turned out that he was a serial philanderer, had numerous affairs with French women and had unauthorised meetings with the former socialist president, Leon Blum. His case had reached the highest possible levels in government. The then dictator, Chervenkov, took personal interest in it. But then it was dropped.

State security agents realised they had made a mistake and rushed to the address in central Sofia. The postbox with the name of Alexander Ivanov on it was locked. One of them watched it while the other one went to find a locksmith. In that period of time, a well-dressed man arrived at the apartment building, unlocked the box and collected the letter. He was followed to the Foreign Ministry. His identity was established as Alexander Ivanov, diplomat.

The same agent who remembered the name of Alexander Ivanov from the 1950s ran a check on Alexander Ivanov with the Interior Ministry archive on his own initiative. He received a very short report: 'Our Soviet comrades raised suspicion in September 1960 that a member of the delegation accompanying comrade Todor Zhivkov for the 15th Session of the General Assembly of the UN in New York might be an agent of the American CIA.'

A simple check of the members of the delegation produced a name: Alexander Ivanov, member of the technical team.

On 23 May 1962, the Bulgarian secret service (DS) began round the clock surveillance of Alexander Ivanov.

35

2 DECEMBER 1963

From a Letter by Alexander Ivanov to Dora Ivanov

FROM TODAY I HAVE A CELLMATE. I HAD BEEN IN THE CELL on my own since my arrest two months ago and I am grateful for some company. He is an uneducated man who pretends to be a common criminal caught by accident in some political affair. I know that he is a police informant placed in my cell to observe my behaviour and gain my confidence. I play along and find it amusing. I told him that if I hadn't confessed, neither the KGB nor Bulgarian State Security would've found out anything about my work for the Americans. I know my strengths and I have outwitted them on every count.

He was impressed when I said that in the last two days I had been taken twice to see the interior minister. I didn't tell my cell-mate that I had to capitulate after the first meeting. The minister told me that it would be better for me and for everybody involved in this wretched affair if I confessed. He said that a propaganda trial would be worthless without my confession. If I pleaded not guilty, everything would look staged and the Western press would describe me as the victim of a witch hunt.

Late at night, I lie on my bed in my winter coat. I am cold all the time. There is no heating in the cell. We have one blanket each. When he sleeps, he undresses down to his vest. I wish it were summer again and we were on that lovely sandy beach on the Black Sea. Do you remember the new sanatorium in Golden

Sands where we went last year? If I ever get out of here, we should go there again.

I don't know how much my cellmate knows about politics but I speak freely in front of him about the Soviet Union, China, and Khrushchev's obsession with nuclear weapons. I told him how I impressed the Americans with news about the Russian submarines in Albania. Remember, we heard about it at Professor K.'s dinner party. The Albanians had impounded three Russian submarines after the split with China. Now I stand accused of passing on classified military information to the Americans. Everybody at that party knew about it. But it does not matter. This is going to be a propaganda trial.

Do you think they will change their mind and go ahead with the execution? Zhivkov might use it as a pretext for revenge. You have to be strong, whatever happens to me. The minister said that if I stick to the plan agreed with our Soviet comrades, everything will end up well. Can I trust THEM?

They showed me Lukanov's statement. As foreign minister, he doesn't want to be implicated but I think that at least he tried to be objective. But then he makes a strong accusation against me at the end. He says I have tricked everybody, that I managed to cover my tracks expertly and that that's how I managed to evade capture for such a long time. He offers no explanation about why no one at the ministry acted on the perfidious denouncements against me over the years.

Ambassador Vutov, on the other hand, sticks the knife in. I shall try to question him in court and demolish his tendentious testimony. If he knew that I was a spy, why didn't he tell anybody? He claims that I extracted financial gains by negotiating a bad deal for Bulgaria in our debt talks with the Americans. I was only thrown into the talks because no one else in our delegation spoke English. I shall unmask him as a liar.

This morning I glimpsed a woman walking into the building. I thought it was you. I had been asking for a long time to be allowed to see you and my heart jumped when I saw this woman. She looked exactly like you. I would do anything to see you one more time. Seeing you would give me strength for the trial. I know what is expected of me and I shall give it to them. I even hired two lawyers although I know that any defence in my case will be useless and redundant.

My cellmate is watching me while I am writing this to you. It is the first letter I plucked up the courage to write. I hope that it will reach you. If not, I shall see you at the trial.

With my eternal love,

Yours,

A.

36

2 December 1963

'A regular meeting of the executive board of the International Space Federation took place in one of the conference rooms of Hotel Montherlant in Paris on 24 March this year. I was having coffee in the lobby before the session when George Anderson appeared out of the blue. He said that he was accredited at the conference as a representative of the US State Department. He sat down next to me and went straight to the point.

'"We have confidential information that there are preparations in Sofia for a trial against the deposed prime minister, Anton Yugov, and his associates," he said.

'According to the CIA, I, too, was among the people to be indicted. Would I be able to find out more about these trials? I replied with a deep sigh that I was not in a position to find that out. Such trials would normally be discussed only among the very few of Zhivkov's confidants in collaboration with the KGB and the head of Bulgarian State Security. I had no access to these people.

'"I am sure that if you tried you might be able to glean some information from secondary sources," Anderson said. "If such trials are being prepared, we might be able to prevent them either through the media or by other means. In this way, we may be able to help you stay alive. We in the United States are very keen to have democracy established in Eastern Europe, which will be a guarantee for peace and stability in the world."

'I relented. He offered me two cypher sheets – one for coding, the other for decoding. Then he started to explain how to work with them but I stopped him and said that I was familiar with this type of work. I had used such sheets during my work at our embassy in Paris and at our mission at the UN. He wrote several radio wavelengths on the back of one of the sheets and said that I should receive the messages on shortwave. Did I still have a shortwave radio transmitter and receiver in Sofia? I said I did. He wrote down the hours and minutes of the transmissions. Finally, he gave me an address in New York for posting my responses to if I couldn't send radio messages. They would send me by post a special carbon-copy sheet with invisible ink for my response.

'I was so disturbed by the news that there would be a political trial against Yugov and his friends, including me, that I mechanically agreed to do everything Anderson asked of me.

'According to Anderson's instructions, the CIA would be sending me coded messages every first and third Friday of the month at 9.30 p.m. I made several efforts to receive those messages on the agreed wavelength but failed. My Hammarlund radio receiver, which also had a built-in transmitter, didn't work very well. I had bought it in the US in 1958.

'In May 1963 I was on a business trip to the United States. On one occasion Anderson stopped me in the corridors at the UN headquarters and said they hadn't sent me the invisible ink sheet because they were worried about my safety. I didn't ask why but assumed that they knew our embassy in Paris had applied for a US visa for me and that they didn't want their letter received while I was out of the country.

'I sent only one message back to the CIA, a letter to a secret address in Lausanne, Switzerland, not the address in New York. It simply said that there would be no trial against Yugov.

'I wrapped one of the code sheets in a gauze dressing and left it in the drawer of the bookcase in the sitting room. The other I put among some files with my work. The address in New York was written in my black leather diary, impounded during my arrest.

'And lastly, the CIA had devised a plan for my extraction from Bulgaria if I felt that my life was in danger. All I had to do was send a telegram to either the address in Lausanne or in New York with the words, "Cable urgently the day of your departure." I was assured that somebody would be in touch about when and how I would be taken out of Bulgaria for a new life in the West. Needless to say, I never tried to use this extraction procedure.'

37

3 December 1963

'Good morning,' Major Ohridski began the daily interrogation session. 'We are nearing the end of the investigative process. The prosecution needs three weeks to prepare for the trial.'

'Oh, good, I am looking forward to it. I am ready,' Alexander replied, hardly a trace of enthusiasm in his voice. 'There was no hot water this morning. I haven't had a shower for three days now. And my cellmate smells. Can you let him have a shower, too?'

'We'll see what we can do. We didn't have any hot water in our apartment this morning, either. There must be a breakdown in the central supply somewhere.' The major sounded almost guilty: 'But shall we start with a meeting you had with General Yazov in September of last year? Do you remember such a meeting?'

'Yes, I remember it very well. I went to see him ahead of the Fifth International Congress of the International Space Federation, due to be held in our country. I was among the nominees for the Federation's next president. Our Soviet comrades supported my nomination.'

'Yes, and with a cursory look at the minutes of the proceedings one would find that your most ardent supporter at the congress was the head of the American delegation, Andrew Haley. Why do you think that was?'

'Of course the Americans wanted me to lead the organisation. I was the most qualified person for the job.'

'Did you discuss your nomination with Cyril Black or anyone else from the CIA?'

'Yes, I did. After my failure to join the UN as a permanent undersecretary, the CIA promised to support me in getting the job at the Space Federation. But may I remind you I wasn't elected just because the Americans supported me. It was our Soviet comrades who cast the decisive vote. I wanted to turn the Federation into a vibrant organisation that would work out the legal framework for future space exploration. I wanted to move the headquarters from Paris to Sofia. The Central Committee and the Bulgarian Academy of Sciences gave me their support.'

Alexander paused. He remembered the exhilarating foreign trips he had undertaken on behalf of the Federation. This was a project close to his heart. He was at the centre of it and enjoyed the limelight. He remembered the starry-eyed intelligent young people burning with a desire to work for the peaceful exploration of outer space. He remembered Olga, a scientist and a lover, the hotel in Moscow and the unpleasantness of his arrest.

'That's all very well,' the major slowed his words, as if thinking about something else. 'My question really is about why you made the offer to the deputy head of State Security, General Yazov, to become an operative of the Bulgarian Foreign Intelligence Service. You volunteered. Did the Americans ask you to do that?'

Alexander stumbled. He wasn't prepared for this. He would never have thought that the contents of such a private and very sensitive conversation would find its way into the files. He went to Yazov in a personal capacity. He didn't go through the official channels. This could only have been placed in the major's file by a very high authority. His approach to Yazov and the Geshev scheme were inextricably linked. Did the major know more than he was letting on?

Alexander was faced with a dilemma: either confirm that it was indeed the CIA who prompted him (the easy option) or open a new can of worms and tell the truth – that Geshev had been the one pulling the strings. He never mentioned Geshev's name to anyone. But what if their meeting in Rome was known to the powers that be? Perhaps it was the Soviet KGB that followed them to Piazza Barberini? The KGB had been known to go around Bulgarian Intelligence and communicate directly with the party leader. And what if some of the people he had already approached with Geshev's offer had got cold feet and shopped him to Zhivkov. Even if that were the case, it was unlikely that the major should be privy to such information. It wasn't Zhivkov's style nor was it in his interest to tell anybody outside his inner circle.

Suddenly, it dawned on him that Zhivkov knew. It all made sense. He wasn't going to be punished for espionage. He wasn't going to be punished for sending one coded radio transmission to the CIA in Athens, which simply said that there would be no trial against Yugov. Zhivkov was going to use this trial to get rid of him because one of the people he approached with Geshev's idea must have betrayed him. But who was it?

Geshev's plan was simple. Approach people with real power but outside Zhivkov's immediate circle, people who openly disliked him. Like General A., for example, the commander of the tank regiment on the outskirts of Sofia. He felt left out and thought he deserved a higher position. The regiment had played its part in three successful putsches in the last four decades. He loved the idea that Zhivkov would be unmasked as a police informant. The Fox would lose support and his demise would be spectacular. Other hated figures around him would fall with him. That was a sweet thought.

In all, Alexander had only approached three people: two generals and a member of the Central Committee. Alexander relied on the idea that none of them would go back to Zhivkov and spill the beans because that would implicate them. 'Why did they choose you for their conspiracy?' would be the first question to be asked. There was no good answer to such a question. In the long run, you're either dead or comfortably retired. That would depend on how well you convince the Fox of your loyalty.

It must have been one of the generals. They all want power, but when offered an opportunity they turn into cowards. At any rate, the game of influence, the most difficult game in all spy games, was over.

A strange calmness enveloped him. This was the end. The Fox had outmanoeuvred him. That was neat: killing two birds with one stone, obliging the Russians with a propaganda trial and getting rid of a conspiracy to unseat him in one go. He should've known better. The Soviets didn't care about whether Zhivkov had been a police informant before the Red Army invaded Bulgaria. They only cared about having a loyal servant dancing to their tune now.

'It was the CIA who had asked me to do that,' Alexander said quietly.

The major was visibly relieved. He closed the thick cardboard file on the desk in front of him and stared at Alexander.

'My job here is done,' he said with sadness in his voice, as if reluctant to end the interrogation. 'I shall see you in court. The trial is scheduled for 26 December.'

'Thank you, major. You are an honest man, but don't let the system corrupt you. I have seen it happen to many honest people. It is so easy to fall into that trap, especially when you are angry. This is what I did, but I did it for noble reasons. I believed that there should be equilibrium between the two systems in the world – communist and capitalist. No side should be under the illusion that it has an advantage. Yes, I helped the Americans with information. But I also helped our side. Finally, you have to believe me that I never took money from the Americans for myself. I have always taken it to give to other people.'

The major was about to offer a handshake, but changed his mind. The duty officer led Alexander away.

~

Four days after Alexander Ivanov's death sentence was pronounced, at the firing range of Sofia Central Prison, the stout man with the rough face was led in front of the firing squad. He refused a blindfold. The verdict of the court was read out by an unnamed official. The commander of the firing squad gave the order. The man stared at the faces of the eleven young soldiers pointing their rifles at him. They fired. Alexander Ivanov slumped to his knees.

Out of eleven bullets only two hit the target – one in the stomach, the other in the thigh. The body gently rolled on to its side, eyes still facing the firing squad. A streak of blood appeared at the corner of the mouth. The legs began to convulse.

He lay there in silence for a few seconds. Droplets of sweat appeared on the forehead of the official who had read out the verdict. The sheet of paper trembled in his hand. No protocol existed about what to do in such circumstances.

Alexander lifted his body on a weak elbow and looked the chief prosecutor in the eye.

'Please, finish me off. You owe me this favour. I saved your life…'

The chief prosecutor was a hard man. He himself had only just escaped the death squads twenty-odd years ago when he was tried for sedition by the wartime fascist regime. Many of his friends, Alexander's friends, had been murdered during the resistance. He had seen severed heads impaled on wooden poles in the main square of his village. But now an invisible hand had grabbed him by the throat. He didn't know what to do.

The man standing next to him unbuttoned his jacket to reveal a German Luger with a brown grip – a trophy by the look of it, captured from a Nazi trooper. He pulled it from the leather holster and shot Alexander in the back of the head from close range. One of the soldiers from the firing squad threw up. It was a messy affair and everybody was glad when it was all over. Alexander's body was swiftly bundled into an unmarked grave in the prison grounds.

No one paid any attention to the pale man in the green uniform from the Committee for State Security who stood a few feet away from the main group of officials during the botched execution. No one knew why he was there. His name was Major Ivan Ohridski, thirty-eight, the chief investigator in the case for espionage against Alexander Ivanov.

Outside the prison walls, across the capital city, in factories and offices, people went about their business unaware of what had just happened. It was a grim winter's day. A black Russian-made Volga limousine left the Central Prison and slowly sailed along the wet cobblestone streets towards the grand building of the Communist Party Central Committee. The windows at the rear and on the passenger sides of the limousine were draped with pleated blue curtains.

There was no traffic because very few people could afford private cars. The black Volga with an official number plate approached the northern side of the granite and limestone building and stopped. A man in the uniform of the People's Militia, the organisation which had replaced the old police force after the communist takeover, saluted and opened the metal gate. The Volga disappeared deep underground.

When the driver eventually stopped at the designated spot, the chief prosecutor got out and shook out his crumpled black jacket. He noticed that his hands were trembling. He straightened, took a deep breath and walked towards the lift.

'It's done,' he said, after he was ushered into a grand oak-panelled room.

The man he was addressing stood up from behind the desk, walked over to him, placed his hand on his shoulder and said, 'Good. It had to be done.'

The prosecutor shivered. The soft, white hand tapped his shoulder gently. This hand had already seen many people off. Alexander was just one of them. The Leader was only fifty-two but he had outmanoeuvred much older, more experienced and ruthless communist apparatchiks in the last twenty years. No wonder his nickname was the Fox.

'Did he say anything?' asked the Fox, and his eyes instinctively scanned the room to check if anyone was listening.

'He shouted "Murderers, liars!" when they led him to the firing range, but then he was calm. He was under the impression that the deal was still on... That his life would be spared in return for his confession...' The prosecutor cleared his throat. 'Umm, he thought that it would be a mock execution... and that he would be given a new identity... err, as we agreed...'

'Fine, fine, anything else?'

'Yes, the firing squad couldn't do their job properly... he lay wounded but alive on the ground. Yazov had to finish the job...'

Yazov, the deputy head of State Security who was personally loyal to Zhivkov, could always be relied on. The two went back a long time.

'OK, OK, it's done now. You've done a good job. You must be very tired after all that.'

The prosecutor's ears pricked up when he heard the last words. They sounded ominous.

'Yes, you did a great job and you need a rest. Start packing your suitcases. You are going to New York. It's a well-deserved promotion. The people have decided to make you our man at the United Nations.'

It took a few seconds for the chief prosecutor to digest the news. They want me out of the way, he thought. They may even blame me one day for the death of Alexander Ivanov. A nice diplomatic post was a sinecure to shut up anybody who knew too much.

'I'm ready to serve the people wherever they send me,' he said.

'Good, good,' Zhivkov said mildly. 'Have you put all the documents of the Ivanov case in a single file?'

Zhivkov, the Leader, also known as Number One or even Daddy in later years, was famous for giving only verbal orders. No written instructions, no paper trail. His signature was reserved for parliamentary decrees, diplomatic appointments and international treaties.

'Yes, I have ordered all departments to send me the papers, comrade Zhivkov.'

'Good, good. You must make sure there are no stray documents lurking in any departments. When everything is in the file, you must bring it to me personally. Can you do that?'

'Aye, comrade.'

'Now, who else knows the details of the case as well as you do?'

'The chief investigator, Major Ohridski. He arrested Alexander and conducted the questioning.'

'Is he one of us?'

'Aye, comrade. He is very loyal,' responded the prosecutor somewhat stiffly.

'Hmm.' Zhivkov looked directly in his eyes. 'What makes him tick? What does he want?'

'I think he wants to be a writer. He wants to write a screenplay for a spy film,' the chief prosecutor said.

'Well, well, well, an intellectual, is he? That's easy. Make him a writer. Also, send a recommendation to the head of the secret service to promote him to colonel for his excellent work on the case. I'll take it from here.'

38

DORA IVANOV

ONE MONTH AFTER ALEXANDER'S EXECUTION, I WAS VISITED by Yazov in Sofia. He and Zhivkov went back a long way. There was something murky in their past which made them stick together. He said he was paying me a visit as a private individual, not as the deputy head of the Committee for State Security. There were dark rumours about his role in the setting up of the labour camps after the coup of 9 September 1944. People said he was far too eager to have people tortured and murdered in the camps. His role in the resistance also lay shrouded in mystery. The people he worked with had either been killed or had disappeared soon after the 9 September coup.

Yazov wanted me to know that *they* found it unbelievable that I didn't know about Alexander's activities as a spy. There was no evidence against me, he said, except one piece of information, which had just come to light.

In the spring of 1963, Alexander was under surveillance and our new apartment in Zaimov Park had already been bugged for a few months. The apartment was Alexander's pride and joy. It was on the sixth floor of the tallest residential building in Sofia and afforded spectacular views over the capital. The location was exclusive, too, just one block away from where Zhivkov and his closest ministers lived. One of our neighbours in the apartment building was the world-famous Bulgarian opera singer, Nicolai Ghiaurov. Ghiaurov, a thirty-four-year-old bass, had just been

signed for a season in America. Despite his communist upbringing –
his elder brother was a member of the anti-fascist resistance – he
was nervous about getting his exit visa, a de facto permission to
travel to the West.

One day he was tuning his radio set when, on one of the
medium-wave frequencies, he heard a crackling conversation
between a man and a woman. They spoke Bulgarian. He immediately realised that he had picked up a radio transmitter in his
own building, which could mean only one thing – his flat had been
bugged. Furious, but at the same time anxious that his American
contract might be in jeopardy, he jumped into his car and drove
to the Interior Ministry. There, he demanded to see the deputy
minister and head of the Committee for State Security, Angel
Solakov. Being a world-famous opera singer and part of a venerable
communist dynasty he was seen at once.

'Why are you bugging my apartment?' His face was red, trying
to hold back his booming voice. 'I've just picked up a conversation
from a local transmitter in my own building. It can only mean
one thing. Don't deny it because I know what I'm talking about.'

Solakov didn't deny it. He explained that it wasn't him that the
secret police were eavesdropping on. Reassured that he wasn't the
target and that it was one of his neighbours in trouble with the
authorities, Ghiaurov left.

'But the story didn't end there,' Yazov told me, lifting his eye-
brow. 'Solakov asked for the transcript of the bugging device in
Alexander's apartment on that day. There was nothing recorded.
Familiar with the erratic performance of his agents, he sent
someone to ask Ghiaurov whether he could recall what was said
in the conversation he had inadvertently overheard. The agent
reported that the woman had said, "You are throwing your life
and career away," and the man responded, "Don't worry, I've got
something on them. No one would dare touch me."'

I remembered these words. Alexander and I frequently had this type of exchange. I told Yazov that I was referring to Alexander's many affairs. I said he never explained to me what it was that he had, and who he was supposed to blackmail. He always said that it was for my own good that I was kept in the dark. Yazov believed me and I was left alone. Except for an anonymous letter a few months later. Our new modern apartment in Zaimov Park had been confiscated and I had moved to an house on the edge of the Freedom Park. The propaganda frenzy against Alexander had subsided and I was trying to get back to my normal life.

Alexander had firmly believed that he'd struck a deal – he would be spared execution in exchange for a full (and embellished) confession and a suicidal public admission of guilt in court. Until the last minute he thought the trial was a propaganda charade and he was just play-acting. Before his last word in court I did warn him not to make an incriminating speech because this was how he would be remembered. He replied that everything would be fine. I warned him, too, not to allow his life to be rewritten and tainted with false accusations and false confessions. But he wouldn't listen. I don't know whether he was a spy or not. As with other things in his life, it wasn't clear to me what was fantasy and what was real.

The anonymous letter was nothing to do with politics or espionage. It contained a carbon copy of a tightly typed page from the interrogation of one of the witnesses for the prosecution, Gina D. I'd met Gina in 1950 in Paris when Alexander was a counsellor and charge d'affaires. She was the wife of the culture attaché and worked as a typist at the embassy. She was only twenty. Her much older husband was a well-known revolutionary writer and literary critic from before the war. I didn't know the family very well: we didn't socialise with them, neither then nor after our return from

Paris. The transcript of Gina's statement to the interrogators was shocking:

I knew Alexander Ivanov from Paris when he was a counsellor in our legation after the war. I was there with my husband and I can't say that our two families were very close. He knew my husband from their student years when they were engaged in the revolutionary struggle. My husband suggested many times that we should invite Alexander and his wife for dinner but I resisted. I used to say to him, 'Stay away from Alexander. He used to work at the Interior Ministry. You know what kind of people worked there after the revolution. They are dangerous.' My husband has always been a rebel even since the revolution. He would say something against the new regime and that would be taken directly to State Security. It would be put on file. However, despite all that, rightly or wrongly I fell in love with Alexander. It's not shameful or obscene to admit that I fell in love with him, is it? I loved him but I don't think he knew then that I was attracted to him. My contact with him was restricted to official duties. My stomach tightened every time I went into his office with letters for signature. I knew that I was in love with him.

Our sexual relationship began when we accidentally met six years later in Sofia. In 1956 he was a professor at the law faculty. Unfortunately, very soon after our first meeting he was sent to America and we only communicated by letter. I can't remember anything that may be of use to your investigation except one thing. When he returned from America in 1962 he was very angry. Although still allowed to travel to the West, he had to get approval for each and every trip. One day he was very angry that one of his foreign trips hadn't been approved and he said, 'I'll hurt them so much that THEY will remember me for life.' I don't know why but this made a big impression on me. He continued: 'I have already hurt them once but I'll hit them again so that THEY won't forget it.' I didn't know who he was talking about. Who were 'THEY'? I didn't think it was a particular person or persons. I thought that he was talking about our whole government, the system, the country.

Otherwise, we didn't talk much about politics. Normally, he would pick me up in his car, a brand new Mercedes Benz, from a street in the centre of Sofia and if the weather was good he would drive to the nearby mountain. In the car, we would talk about the time we met in Paris. He would say that he liked me from the moment he set eyes on me. I would say that I fell in love with him in Paris but didn't know how to tell him. Once we arrived at his favourite place in the mountain, the Golden Bridges, he would take a blanket from the car and we would go to a secluded spot. Inevitably, he would ask me if I still liked him even though he was much older than me. I would reply that I loved him because he was intelligent and cultured, and very sophisticated. He would embrace me and I would reciprocate. After making love, we would take a short walk around the big boulders – an area which looked like a big river of stone – and then we would return to Sofia.

Other times, he would invite me to his place when his wife was not there; first to his old house, and later to his new apartment in the best new building in Sofia, an apartment block in Zaimov Park right in the centre of the city. We would begin with a conversation about why we liked each other and whether there was still love between the two of us; then we would embrace and kiss, and eventually make love on the couch. It was always the couch, never on the bed in the bedroom. Our encounters never lasted more than an hour. He always kept our meetings to schedule.

A few times he took me to another apartment in the centre, which he said belonged to his family's former maid. He had his own key to that apartment. Again, the couch, again one hour. And yes, he always gave me some money to help with my expenses.

By the time I finished reading, tears were rolling down my face. Although I knew that he was seeing other women during our marriage, the level of detail was like a knife in my stomach. I hated and loved him at the same time. This was the way I remembered him, the love of my life – reckless, frivolous and always thinking only of himself. The world was there to please him, not the other way around.

I suspected that this letter was sent by 'THEM'. They wanted me to know that they could hurt me at any time and in any way. It was a warning that I shouldn't rock the boat. And I didn't. A few months after Alexander's execution, I was allowed to take up a job with the Institut Pasteur in Paris. Madame Bovren helped me secure the job. We became good friends until her death. I worked in France for many years until my retirement.

We never talked about Alexander. He was truly forgotten.

And I never said anything to anyone – until now.

EPILOGUE

MAJOR OHRIDSKI WAS PROMOTED TO COLONEL SHORTLY after Alexander's execution. He retired from the secret service a few years later to dedicate himself to writing. He was well looked after; free holidays to writers' retreats in the mountains or by the sea, conferences and events, banquets and cocktail parties in return for occasional articles in selected small-circulation publications. He only wrote one spy-thriller screenplay which was made into a film. The main character was a young Bulgarian counter-espionage operative who exposes an American conspiracy to undermine the socialist state and saves a young woman about to be killed by a foreign intelligence agency. Although his name appeared on the credits as the writer, by the time the film was shown in the cinemas it bore little resemblance to the story he wrote. He eventually realised that under Zhivkov writers were paid not to write. He retreated into drinking with former colleagues in hunting lodges and seaside chalets, and eventually faded into oblivion.

Zhivkov's tactic of promoting the people he disliked before sending them into comfortable retirement paid off. This was the way he dealt with enemies and potential rivals alike. Far from being put on trial, Yugov received his full ministerial pension, which was topped up with an official limousine and a driver, and free access to otherwise restricted military clubs and restaurants reserved for the nomenklatura. He partied with thick-necked bodyguards and killers of the past into a ripe old age. He saw the demise of Zhivkov and the fall of communism but it was hard to tell how much of it he understood.

Yazov never made it to the top echelons of power. He died an embittered murderer whose efforts were never appreciated by those he served. The chief prosecutor, who saw Alexander's trial to its conclusion, was rewarded with a string of diplomatic sinecures.

All their children were allowed to prosper.

After the demise of Khrushchev, Zhivkov turned Bulgaria into Moscow's most loyal satellite. In return, he was allowed to rule as he pleased. Apart from a small military plot against him a year after Alexander's death, there was no resistance to his rule. The plotters' were the last political executions carried out during his regime. He lavished gifts on his supporters and pardoned his enemies. My father was among the many political detainees who survived the labour camps, eventually to be released from enforced internal exile. He returned to the capital, Sofia, where I grew up.

When Zhivkov died, there was a palpable degree of sympathy among the population. Today, there is a monument to Zhivkov at the museum in his home town. The inscription on a polished black marble plaque reads, 'I used all my power for the prosperity of my people.'

Alexander Ivanov was airbrushed from history during Zhivkov's rule. In post-communist Bulgaria, there was little interest in his life, and what interest there was was mainly confined to the pages of the popular press. He was considered a political victim at best, a traitor at worst. The Americans never acknowledged him as one of their assets.

ACKNOWLEDGEMENTS

I am indebted to the staff of the Bulgarian National Library, St Cyril & St Methodius, in Sofia, for their kindness in allowing me to peruse the archive for material about the trial of the real-life spy, Ivan-Asen Georgiev.

I would like to single out two publications that have contributed to this work: *Materials from the Trial for Espionage against Ivan-Asen Georgiev* by Nikolai Nachev (Sofia: Ivrai, 2012) and *The Super-spy Ivan-Asen Georgiev, American Agent or Political Victim?* by Prodan Prodanov (Sofia: Incognito, 2016).

I am forever grateful to my Bulgarian friends P.K. and N.K. for their encouragement and friendship.

AUTHOR'S NOTE

The idea for this book was born out of casual conversations with my friends about what makes a good spy. It is not always true that spies are invisible individuals who do not draw attention to themselves. You only have to look at the exotic allure of Mata Hari, the suave appearance of Richard Sorge, and even the macho appeal of the fictional James Bond.

This is a story based on a quiet and unassuming communist diplomat turned Cold War spy. He spied for the Americans for seven years during the most eventful period in post-war history, in which the world saw the Hungarian Uprising, the Suez Crisis, the Cuban Revolution, the Sino-Soviet split, the U-2 spy plane affair and the Cuban Missile Crisis, to name but a few. His work came to an abrupt end in Moscow in 1963. In the same year, Kim Philby defected to the Soviet Union and a Russian officer, Oleg Penkovsky, was executed by the KGB for passing military secrets to the Americans and the British.

During his work at the UN in New York our spy had access to senior Soviet diplomats and visiting politicians, including the Soviet leader Nikita Khrushchev. Educated in Paris, he spoke several languages effortlessly and was an expert in Roman law. He first came to the attention of American intelligence in Paris while negotiating the peace treaty between the Allied powers and Bulgaria after World War II.

He was a Marxist and a Stalinist, and for many years believed in the communist revolution. But in the mid-1950s he became disillusioned. He witnessed the mismanagement of communist economies and the beginning of the arms race. He found Khrushchev uneducated and unpredictable, and feared that the man was capable of starting a nuclear war. The decision to offer his services to the CIA was a complex one – it involved money, women, foreign travel but, above all, the belief that he was destined to play a huge role in international affairs. He claimed that he was in direct contact with Allen Dulles, the director of the CIA, who valued his opinion. He wrote political analysis and accurate psychological profiles of Soviet and Eastern European leaders. He suffered from grandiose delusions: he harboured ambitions of becoming Secretary-General of the UN. In the last year before his arrest, he became the head of the International Space Federation.

Just when he thought that he had achieved the elevated international position he deserved, the Soviet and Bulgarian secret services caught up with him. He was arrested in Moscow and then handed over to the Bulgarians. He was flown to Sofia and after a short but well-publicised show trial he was executed on 4 January 1964. But was he tricked into making a full confession in return for sparing his life? And how significant was his spying activity?

In this book, you find two viewpoints of the same story. The first is a series of fictional conversations with his widow. I have invented the storyline about meeting Dora by accident in Sofia in the early 1990s when she was eighty-three. The second is a documentary transcript of stenographic notes taken during the interrogation of the real-life spy, Ivan-Asen Georgiev. The ambitious young major in the Bulgarian secret service is a fictional character based on an eponymous prototype. His secret diaries are a product of my imagination. All historical characters and events are true to life.